Metal Building Systems

Metal Building Systems

by the

Metal Building Dealers Association

and the

MBMA

Metal Building Manufacturers Association

Contributing Author:

Computerized Structural Design, Inc.

Milwaukee, Wisconsin

Donald R. Buettner, Ph.D., P.E.

James M. Fisher, Ph.D., P.E.

Curtis B. Miller, M.S., P.E.

ISBN: 0-9603678-0-2

Library of Congress
Catalog Card No.: 79-92478

This publication is designed to provide accurate and authoritative information in regard
to the subject matter covered. It is sold with the understanding that the publisher is not
engaged in rendering legal, accounting, or other professional service. If legal advice or
other expert assistance is required, the services of a competent professional person
should be sought.
—*From a declaration of principles jointly adopted by a committee of the American Bar
Association and a committee of publishers and associations.*

**Printed in the United States of America
Johnson & Hardin Co.**
Cincinnati, Ohio

Acknowledgements

The Publisher wishes to acknowledge the following persons for their assistance in the production of *Metal Building Systems:*

Mr. Robert Baldwin, Technical Publications, Barrington, IL.
Mr. James E. Kessler, CIS International, Leawood, KS.
Mr. A. L. Williams, Metrolina Builders, Charlotte, NC.
Mr. Denny Merry, Peterson Construction Co., Lincoln, NE.
Mr. Jack Steinberger, Steinberger Construction Co., Logansport, IN.
Mr. William McFarland, Keck, Mahin & Cate, Chicago, IL.
Promotional Services Department, Armco Inc., Middletown, OH.
Butler Manufacturing Co., Kansas City, MO.

Contents

Preface

This book has been developed as a joint and cooperative effort of the Metal Building Dealers Association (MBDA) and Metal Building Manufacturers Association (MBMA). It relates to a need felt by professionals in all phases of the metal building systems business that a comprehensive document be developed to serve the entire industry. This document was intended to include, in one text, an overview of all facets of the metal building systems industry, and to be suitable to a wide range of readership interests. Such a book presented no small challenge to the authors.

The objectives of the book are many, due to the wide readership to which it is directed, and due to the broad range of topics which the Joint Education Committee wanted to include. The Table of Contents illustrates this wide range of topics. The intended readership of *Metal Building Systems* includes builders, manufacturers, contractors, building code officials, architects, engineers, students, and customers. Clearly, not all potential readers may be completely interested in all topics, so the book has been developed so that each chapter essentially stands alone.

The technical information which is included in this book evolved from a variety of sources. The authors' collective experiences played some role, but the major material sources came from the MBDA and MBMA and its member organizations. The authors acknowledge the contributions made by certain members of MBDA and MBMA in providing information which assisted in the development of the technical aspects of each chapter, as well as the enormous support given the authors during the entire development of *Metal Building Systems.*

Joint MBDA & MBMA Education Committee

Members from MBDA

Ray Randolph, Randolph and Son Construction Co. (Chairman)
Michael Schaff, Modsteel Builders
Ken Palmer, Palmer Construction Co., Inc.
Bob Byrne, MBDA Staff
Christopher S. Long, MBDA Staff

Members from MBMA

Lyle Wilson, American Building Co.
Clarke H. Stevenson, National Steel Products Co.
Wilbur Larkin, Butler Manufacturing Co.
Don Johnson, Butler Manufacturing Co.
Fred Petersen, MBMA Staff
Duane Ellifritt, MBMA Staff

Computerized Structural Design, Inc.

Donald R. Buettner, Ph.D., P.E.
James M. Fisher, Ph.D., P.E.
Curtis B. Miller, M.S., P.E.

1
Origin and Growth of Metal Building Systems

History of the Industry

The interaction of several social, political, and technical factors in the middle of the Twentieth Century brought on a relatively new trend in building construction. Or, it might be more appropriate to say that these factors gave renewed vigor to an existing trend. An excess capacity for producing sheet steel, World War II and its resulting material shortage, the urban migration, the need for low-cost and easily portable shelter, the rapid rise in construction labor costs, and the invention of the digital computer, all combined to give momentum to a struggling idea whose time had finally come—the metal building system.

It was not that metal building systems were particularly new in this time period. Some manufacturers had been producing grain bins, garages, and small industrial buildings of light steel construction since 1908, but it wasn't until the late '40's that the metal building systems industry began to make significant inroads into the non-residential low-rise market.

A metal building system was a new application of an old concept. The notion of standardizing parts and producing them in large quantities had been introduced by Eli Whitney in the 1790's in his gun factory in New Haven, Connecticut. Large orders for rifles by the government simply could not be filled by the old method of skilled craftsmen manufacturing one complete weapon at a time—lock, stock, and barrel. Division of labor, standardization of parts, interchangeability, and mass production were necessary to meet the deadline for large quantity orders. One can well imagine that such methods were not welcomed by the gunsmiths' guild, if there was such an organization. These concepts have since been used by most companies that manufacture a consumer product, and of course, are crucial to the metal building systems industry.

Nor should the historical role of other kinds of standardized buildings be overlooked. Pre-fabricated metal houses had been shipped from New England to California during the early days of the Gold Rush to satisfy the critical need for housing. This enterprise was short-lived, however. Once the lumber industry became established in California, metal structures shipped by boat around Cape Horn could no longer compete. During the Franco-Prussian War, factory-made and field assembled metal buildings were used as hospitals.

The first major continuing use of standardized factory buildings was introduced by the Samuel Austin and Son Company of Cleveland, Ohio (now the Austin Company), in 1917. Ten standard designs were developed and a catalog produced from which a customer could choose the size and type that met his needs. The structural system consisted of steel columns and roof trusses in modular sizes which had already been designed, detailed, and in some cases, fabricated. This concept of doing the engineering work before the sale, later to become known as "Pre-engineering," meant that the customer got his building shipped to the job site several weeks earlier, because of time saved in the design stage. Austin marketed these standardized buildings throughout the United States and established district sales offices for this purpose, probably the first engineering and construction company to do so.

One of the major developments that helped to bring about the rapid growth of metal building systems was the emergence of cold-formed steel as structural members. After the 1870's, the economical production of rolled steel beams and columns began a new era in construction. The massive stone bearing wall buildings gradually began to give way to steel skeleton frameworks covered with light wall coverings. Cold-formed sheet steel was used then but only for non-structural applications, such as wall coverings. In the 1930's, the country found itself with an excess capacity for sheet steel production and not enough markets. It was during this period that the American Iron and Steel Institute began sponsorship of research at Cornell University, under Dr. George Winter, to formulate design guidelines for structural components made from cold-formed sheets. Many years of research eventually led to the publication of the first design specification for cold-formed light-gauge steel in 1946. An authoritative design specification, backed up by years of research, meant that for the first time, buildings of light gauge steel could be designed without resorting to tests.

Any discussion of the history of the metal building systems industry must include the Quonset Hut®, despite the negative connotation that it represents to modern metal building systems manufacturers. The Quonset Hut was named for the Naval Base at Quonset Point, Rhode Island, and was developed to fill a military need for a shelter that could be easily constructed by unskilled labor using only hand tools, could be built in remote areas, and could be easily disassembled and transported to a new location and re-used. The familiar half-round structure that has, in some minds, forever saddled metal building systems with the image of cheapness and questionable workmanship, was built by the thousands all over the world by Allied troops in the '40's. Many are still being used today. Although these buildings were certainly not the first metal buildings, they represent the greatest effort at standardizing and mass production up to that time and were easily the best remembered.

In the post-war years, the metal building system was characterized by galvanized sheet steel roof and wall panels, moderate spans, light framing or self-framing, a roof slope of around 4/12, and a look of functional utility. Not much thought was given to aesthetics because the market was largely industrial and agricultural.

By 1960, pre-painted panels had been developed and gave the customer a choice of several attractive colors. The first painted panels were sprayed, then baked, as with an automobile body, but, later on, the technology of coil coating improved to the extent that all painted panels were able to be formed from previously painted coils.

When the industry was young, architects were, in general, not favorably disposed toward metal building systems, but economic necessity, coupled with the rapid growth rate of the metal building systems industry caused a gradual change in attitude. Today, many metal building systems are designed or specified by architectural firms. Other materials, such as stone, glass, and wood, are combined with the basic metal building system in creating attractive buildings for commerce, recreation and public use.

The importance of the digital computer to the metal building systems industry cannot be overstated. The repetition and standardization inherent in this kind of product made it a natural application for computer analysis. Programs could easily be standardized to fit the structural types, standard loads and load combinations that had formerly been laboriously cranked out on a desk calculator. Structural analysis computer programs were first written in the 1950's, utilizing first-generation computers, such as the IBM 650. Applications soon spread from structural analysis to bills of material and detailing work.

As computer technology advanced into second and third generations and plotters and interactive graphics came on the scene, metal building systems manufacturers adapted their operations to find uses for these new aids. It is common today to find that for a given job, the structural analysis, design, bill of material, fabrication drawings and erection drawings are produced totally or in large part by computer. The accelerating growth of the metal building systems industry, roughly paralleling that of improvements in computer technology, has been accompanied by trends to wider, single-gabled buildings, lower roof slopes, improved roof systems, better thermal performance and improved appearance through the imaginative use of color and other materials.

On June 28, 1956, the representatives of five metal building system manufacturing companies met in Chicago to organize a trade association. In December of that year, the Metal Building Manufacturers Association was formed with thirteen charter members. The Association organized several committees and set about the task of dealing with problems common to all members, concerning structural design, fire, insurance, building codes, transportation, and safety. Programs of sponsored research in structural behavior and fire performance since 1970 have established the professional credibility and technical competence of the engineers in the industry and have led to many major improvements in the state-of-the-art of structural design.

Probably the single factor that sets this industry apart from other methods of construction is the way in which metal building systems are marketed, sold, and erected. In the 1950's, some manufacturers began a movement which rapidly spread through the entire industry. The new way of doing business was to sell a building, not directly to a customer, but through a franchised builder who would act as a general contractor providing erection service as well. A metal building system was different from conventional steel construction and the problems encountered in erection were not generally understood by the average iron worker. Quick erection and occupancy was, and still is, one of the chief advantages of a metal building system, so it was necessary to eliminate anything that slowed down the process. The franchised builder, trained by the manufacturer in the construction of his building, seemed to be the ideal solution to a lot of problems. The idea spread rapidly and in 1968, the Metal Building Dealers Association was organized. There are today about 8,800 metal building system contractors in the United States.

Growth of the Industry

Metal building system sales have grown from an estimated $25 million in 1947 to $250 million in 1966 and over $1 billion in 1978*. The metal building systems industry has become the fastest growing segment of the consturction industry. The stimulus for this growth has been the increasing acceptance of metal building systems for commercial applications and community

*which represents over $6 billion of in-place construction.

facilities, due to the fact that metal building systems are marketed (instead of bid) by over 8,800 builders. In earlier years, the main markets were primarily in agricultural and manufacturing applications. It is estimated that over 47% of all single story, non-residential construction is built with metal building systems today. This percentage will surely increase in the future.

Factors Affecting Growth

The primary reason for the rapid growth of the metal building systems industry is economics. Overall construction and maintenance costs are lower than those of the competition. Building construction is the most "labor oriented" segment of the construction industry and, at the same time, the least automated. The metal building systems industry has successfully reduced the amount of field labor required to erect a building through in-plant automation and a systems approach to building design. The manufacturer fabricates a metal building system consisting of pre-cut and pre-punched elements that can be erected in less time than it takes to construct other building systems. The contractor is responsible for selling and building the completed system. The shift from onsite field labor to factory labor has produced significant savings because factory labor costs have not increased as rapidly as field labor costs.

Not only are construction and field labor costs reduced, but material costs are also reduced. Manufacturers use computers* to perform analysis and design which enables them to fabricate structural members with maximum strength-to-weight ratios. The wasted material that results from using standard rolled sections (with uniform section properties) is minimized. The framing system used in metal building systems requires a less extensive foundation, because the walls are non-load bearing. Most significant, however, is the fact that a large portion of the entire metal building system construction process is done under factory control where efficiency and quality can be exercised to a much greater degree than in the field.

The design-build concept adopted by many metal building system contractors has also affected the growth of the metal building systems industry. The manufacturer's automated fabrication

---

*This use of computers may be the single most important factor in the growth of the metal building systems industry.

of building system components provides a tighter control over production costs. This enables a contractor to quote and guarantee a firm price to the customer for his building. The contractor's familiarity and past experience with a manufacturer's system also enables him to accurately predict both erection costs and erection time to the owner. As a result, the builder has the ability to quote both a price and a completion date for a building with a high degree of accuracy.

The continual improvement and expansion of the metal building system also has had a tremendous impact on growth. The many available products offer a wide variety of design possibilities that reach a broader customer base. The fact that metal building systems are used in almost half of all single story, non-residential construction means that metal building systems have become *the* conventional way to build. Today an owner can get a metal building system that in no way resembles the old stereotype "tin shed." Outstanding architectural design can and is being achieved in an all-metal building system. Also, combinations of other building materials (glass, masonry, and concrete) with factory produced metal systems (trusses, frames, roofs, walls, and floors) have created many architecturally appealing structures. Architects have used metal building systems to replace conventional component structural systems at considerable cost savings.

Computerization in the manufacturing process is another factor which caused a substantial growth in the industry. Automated fabrication techniques are computer operated. The result is faster production with increased quality control.

Markets for Metal Building Systems

The principal markets for metal building systems are commercial, manufacturing, community facilities, and agriculture. A breakdown of the distribution of sales in these markets in 1978 is shown below:

Commercial: Warehousing, retail stores, offices and banks, garages, transportation facilities....................... 38.3%

Manufacturing: Production, warehousing, and equipment service facilities 31.1%

Community Facilities: Recreation buildings, schools, churches
.... 9.3%
Agriculture 11.0%
Miscellaneous 10.3%

Metal Building Systems Today

As stated previously, metal building systems represent almost half of all single story non-residential construction. The wide variety of metal building systems available provides an economical solution to most owners' needs. Commercial applications include office buildings, retail stores, automobile showrooms, banks, and theaters. Low-rise, wide span, column- free areas can be created for these applications with the structural systems available by manufacturers. Wall panels are available in a variety of colors and finishes which can be used to architecturally enhance the building. The variety and versatility of the metal building system is responsible for its increased use in the commercial market.

Manufacturing applications of metal building systems include factories, warehouses, utility buildings, freight terminals, and distribution centers. The adaptability of metal building systems to conform to building space requirements is respondible for its extensive use in the manufacturing market. The structural systems available can meet most headroom and clear-span requirements. The building is designed to permit easy future expansion. The wall and roof systems available will provide an energy efficient, watertight, and low maintenance building space for the owner.

Speed of erection and low cost have made metal building systems popular in the community facilities market. Applications include recreational buildings such as skating arenas and tennis courts, schools, churches, and municipal centers. Large column free areas that are typically required in these applications can easily be handled with the available structural systems. The low initial cost and low maintenance cost of metal building systems make them attractive to municipalities working with tax-supported budgets.

The agricultural market was one of the first markets in which metal building systems were used. Shelter and storage buildings are needed in this market, and metal building systems are able to meet these needs most efficiently and economically.

The Future

The success and versatility of the metal building system should both increase its use in existing markets and open up new markets in the future. Continuing research and advance technology in the insulation of roof and wall systems will produce energy efficient buildings which will help owners to deal with energy conservation. The systems approach to building design, fabrication, and erection will help owners to keep building costs to a minimum.

Markets in which the metal building systems industry has had little impact to date are the residential and high-rise markets. These markets may provide opportunity for metal building systems growth. Shortage of materials, high labor costs, and quality control are all problems with which the construction industry has had to deal over the years. The metal building systems industry has successfully dealt with these problems and as a result, has prospered. This success will enable the industry to enter new markets, develop new building systems, and improve production in the future.

2

The Metal Building Systems Industry

There are several participants in the metal building systems industry. These include the manufacturer, the builder, the contractor, the designer, and the owner. Each plays an important role and each interacts in a particular way with the other participants. Certainly not all projects are performed with identical inter-relationships between parties, but the following descriptions are deemed typical.

The Manufacturer

The manufacturer designs and fabricates the metal building system. The design generally includes development of calculations to establish *standardized* member sizes. These members are categorized for various spans, heights, and loadings to accommodate a wide range of building situations. The manufacturer provides catalogs for easy reference as to span and load capabilities of various systems. When a specific project moves into the contract phase for a "going" project, often a customized, computerized analysis and design is made by the manufacturer.

The fabrication phase of the manufacturer's responsibility involves producing columns, beams, frames, posts, purlins, and girts. The frames are welded from steel plate, purlins and girts are formed and cut to the correct length, erection holes are punched or drilled, wall and roof panels are rolled, and all hardware and accessories required for a complete assembly are supplied. After the building is fabricated, it is packaged and shipped to the construction site. Some of the components, such as bolts and other purchased accessories (e.g. doors, windows, etc.), may be manufactured by other suppliers.

The Builder

The builder serves as the general contractor or as a sub-contractor on the project (an increasing number are design-build firms) and provides the metal building system and its erection. The builder works with the owner from first planning through project completion. In the initial stages of a project, the builder will meet with the owner and identify project requirements. At this stage the parties will know the size, shape, and type of building required. The order for the building can then be placed with the manufacturer. After fabrication, the builder will have the structure erected on the site. He may have his own erection crew or deal with another general contractor or independent erector who will provide the erection service. This arrangement has proven to be successful, convenient, and economical for owners since it reduces the number of parties with whom the owner must deal.

In a few instances there is another party present in the industry known as the "broker." The broker sells a building delivered to a job site. The owner would then hire a contractor/builder to erect the building. This arrangement creates more work for the owner which is why the builder arrangement has become more popular today.

The General Contractor

The contractor performs a particular construction service at a job site. Excavating and grading, steel erection, concrete placement and finishing, masonry, carpentry, plumbing, electrical, and heating are different examples of work that the contractor could perform at a given job site. Some contractors (general contractors) will perform several types of work on a given job. Usually a general contractor will hire sub-contractors to perform certain specialized types of work (e.g. electrical, plumbing, etc.).

The Designers — Architects and Engineers

Typically, most jobs will require some engineering and architectural design beyond the scope of that provided by the manufacturer. For example, the design of the foundation system is not normally included with the metal building system. The manufacturer will supply the owner with the forces to be transmitted to the foundation. The owner is then responsible for retaining professional help for that phase of the work. Architectural design may be handled in the same manner.

Many builders classify themselves as "design-build contractors." This means that they coordinate the entire job for an owner including the design. An owner will then have only to deal with one party to get his building built. The design-build contractor will plan the building with the owner, order the building, prepare the site for the building, construct the foundation, erect the building, and install the utilities. Any engineering or architectural work required will be done by either in-house staff engineers or architects, or by arrangement with outside consultants. Any sub-contractors required will be hired by the design-build contractor.

The Owner

The owner is the party who has a need for a building. The owner may be a corporation, a partnership, an individual or business needing new facilities in an expansion move, or an investor developing rental space for profit and tax considerations.

Some owners are sophisticated in the building process and are capable of handling many aspects of the construction. The inexperienced owner may need help at every stage in the building process. There is some "debate" as to whether the design-build (singular responsibility) approach or the architect, contractor, bidding process is better. That issue cannot be settled here. Today many experienced, corporate real estate departments are choosing the design-build route for their projects. The reason is the reduced time required on the part of the owner, and the fact that only one party need be contacted no matter what the problem. In a design-build arrangement, any adverse condition that occurs is the responsibility of the design-build firm. There is no one else to whom the finger may be pointed.

3
Nomenclature

The purpose of this chapter is to define common terminology used in the metal building systems industry that is also used throughout the text. The definitions given are taken from the Metal Building Systems Manual, 1980 Edition, as written by the Metal Building Manufacturers Association Technical Committee.

Basic Terms and Descriptions

Accessory — An extra building product which supplements a basic solid sheeted building such as door, window, skylight, ventilator, etc.

ACI — American Concrete Institute. The organization which has developed the recognized building code for design of concrete structures.

AISI — American Iron and Steel Institute.

AISC — American Institute of Steel Construction.

AISE — American Iron and Steel Engineers.

Aluminum Coated Steel — Steel coated with aluminum for corrosion protection.

ANSI — American National Standards Institute.

Anchor Bolts — Bolts used to anchor structural members to a foundation or other support. Usually refers to the bolts at the bottom of all columns and door jambs.

Anchor Bolt Plan — A plan view showing the size, location, and projection of all anchor bolts for the metal building systems components, the length and width of the foundation (which may vary from the nominal metal building size). Column reactions (magnitude and direction), and minimum base plate dimensions may also be included.

Approval Drawings — Approval drawings may include framing drawings, elevations and sections through the building as furnished by the manufacturer for approval of the buyer. Approval by the buyer affirms that the manufacturer has correctly interpreted the overall contract requirements for the metal building system and its accessories, and the exact location of accessories in the building.

Architectural Drawing — A drawing which shows the plan view and/or elevations of the finished building for the purpose of showing the general appearance of the building, indicating all accessory locations.

ASCE — American Society of Civil Engineers.

Astragal — A closure between the two leaves of a double swing or double slide door to close the joint.

Automatic Welding — A welding operation utilizing a machine to make a continuous, unbroken weld.

Auxiliary Loads — All specified dynamic live loads other than the basic design loads which the building must safely withstand, such as cranes, material handling systems, machinery, elevators, vehicles, and impact loads.

Awning Window — A window in which the vent or vents pivot outward about the top edge giving an awning effect.

AWS — American Welding Society.

Base Angle — An angle secured to the perimeter of the foundation to support and close wall panels.

Base Plate — A plate attached to the base of a column which rests on the foundation or other support, usually secured by anchor bolts.

Bay — The space between frame center lines or primary supporting members in the longitudinal direction of the building.

BBC — Basic Building Code (see BOCA).

Beam — A primary member, usually horizontal, that is subjected to bending loads. There are three types: simple, continuous, and cantilever.

Beam and Column — A primary structural system consisting of a series of rafter beams supported by columns. Often used as the end frame of a metal building system.

10

Bearing Plate — A steel plate that is set on the top of a masonry support on which a beam or purlin can rest.

Bent — The primary member of a structural system.

Bill of Materials — A list of items or components used for fabrication, shipping, receiving, and accounting purposes.

Bird Screen — Wire mesh used to prevent birds from entering the building through ventilators and louvers.

Blind Rivet — A small headed pin with expandable shank for joining light gauge metal. Typically used to attach flashing, gutter, etc.

Block or Board Thermal Insulation — Rigid or semi-rigid thermal insulation preformed into rectangular units.

BOCA — Building Officials and Code Administrators International, Inc.

Bonded Roof — A roof which carries a written warranty with respect to weather-tightness for a stipulated number of years.

Brace Rods — Rods or cables used in roof and walls to transfer loads, such as wind loads, and seismic and crane thrusts to the foundation. (Also often used to plumb buildings but not designed to replace erection cables.)

Bracket — A structural support projecting from a wall or column on which to fasten another structural member. Examples are canopy brackets, lean-to brackets, and crane runway brackets.

Bridge Crane — A load lifting system consisting of a hoist which moves laterally on a beam, girder, or bridge which in turn moves longitudinally on a runway made of beams and rails. Loads can be moved to any point within a rectangle formed by the bridge span and runway length.

British Thermal Unit (BTU) — That amount of heat required to raise the temperature of one pound (2.2 kg) of water by 1° F. (0.56° C.).

Builder/Contractor — A general contractor or sub-contractor responsible for providing and erecting metal building systems.

Building Code — Regulations established by a recognized agency describing design loads, procedures, and construction details for structures. Usually applying to designated political jurisdiction (city, county, state, etc.)

Built-Up Roofing — A roof covering made up of alternating layers of tar and asphaltic materials.

Built-Up Section — A structural member, usually an "I" section, made from individual flat plates welded together.

Butt Plate — The end plate of a structural member usually used to rest against a like plate of another member in forming a connection. Sometimes called a split plate or bolted end plate.

"C" Section — A member formed from steel sheet in the shape of a block "C", that may be used either singularly or back to back.

Camber — A predetermined curvature designed into a structural member to offset the anticipated deflection when loads are applied.

Canopy — Any overhanging or projecting roof structure with the extreme end usually unsupported.

Cantilever — A projecting beam that is supported and restrained at one end only.

Capillary Action — That action which causes movement of liquids when in contact with two adjacent surfaces such as panel sidelaps.

Cap Plate — A plate located at the top of a column or end of a beam for capping the exposed end of the member.

Caulk — To seal and make weather-tight the joints, seams, or voids by filling with a waterproofing compound or material.

Channel - Hot Rolled — A member formed while in a semi-molten state at the steel mill to a shape having standard dimensions and properties.

Clip — A plate or angle used to fasten two or more members together.

Closure Strip — A resilient strip, formed to the contour of ribbed panels used to close openings created by joining metal panels and flashing.

Cold Forming — The process of using press brakes or rolling mills to shape steel into desired cross sections at room temperature.

Collateral Load — All specified additional dead loads other than the metal building framing, such as sprinklers, mechanical and electrical systems, and ceilings.

Column — A primary member used in a vertical position on a building to transfer loads from main roof beams, trusses, or rafters to the foundation.

Continuity — The terminology given to a structural system denoting the transfer of loads and stresses from member to member, as if there were no connections.

Contractor — See Builder.

Covering — The exterior roof and wall covering for a metal building system.

Crane — A machine designed to move material by means of a hoist.

Crane Rail — A track supporting and guiding the wheels of a bridge crane or trolley system.

Crane Runway Beam — The member that supports a crane rail and is supported by columns or rafters depending on the type of crane system. On underhung bridge cranes, a runway beam also acts as crane rail.

Curb — A raised edge on a concrete floor slab or skylight.

Curtain Wall — Perimeter wall panels which carry only their own weight and wind load.

Damper — A baffle used to open or close the throat of ventilators.

Dead Load — The dead load of a building is the weight of all permanent construction, such as floor, roof, framing, and covering members.

Deflection — The displacement of a structural member or system under load.

Design Loads — Those loads specified in building codes published by Federal, State, County, or City agencies, or in owner's specifications to be used in the design of a building.

Diagonal Bracing — See Brace Rods.

Diaphragm Action — The resistance to racking generally offered by the covering system, fasteners, and secondary framing.

Door Guide — An angle or channel guide used to stabilize or keep plumb a sliding or rolling door during its operation.

Downspout — A conduit used to carry water from the gutter of a building to the ground or storm drain.

Drift Pin — A tapered pin used during erection to align holes in steel members to be connected by bolting.

Eave — The line along the sidewall formed by the intersection of the planes of the roof and wall.

Eave Height — The vertical dimension from finished floor to the eave.

Eave Strut — A structural member at the eave to support roof panels and wall panels. It may also transmit wind forces from roof bracing to wall bracing.

Elastic Design — A design concept utilizing the proportional behavior of materials when all stresses are limited to specified allowable values.

End Frame — A frame at the endwall of a building to support the roof load from one-half the end bay.

Erection — The on-site assembling of fabricated components to form a complete structure.

Erection Drawings — See Framing Drawings.

Expansion Joint — A break or space in construction to allow for thermal expansion and contraction of the materials used in the structure.

Fabrication — The manufacturing process performed in a plant to convert raw material into finished metal building components. The main operations are coldforming, cutting, punching, welding, cleaning, and painting.

Fascia — A decorative trim or panel projecting from the face of a wall.

Fenestration — Windows or other panes of glass; their number and location.

Field — The "job site," "building site," or general market area.

Filler Strip — See Closure Strip.

Finial — Gable closure at ridge.

Fixed Base — A column base that is designed to resist rotation as well as horizontal or vertical movement.

Flange — The projecting edge of a structural member.

Flange Brace — A bracing member used to provide lateral support to the flange of a beam, girder, or column.

Flashing — A sheet metal closure which functions primarily to provide weather-tightness in a structure and secondarily to enhance appearance.

Footing — A pad or mat, usually of concrete, located under a column, wall, or other structural member, that is used to distribute the loads from that member into the supporting soil.

Force — The action of one body on another body which changes or tends to change its state of rest or motion. A force may be expressed in pounds (Newtons), kips, or other similar units and may act in any one of the following ways:
  a. *Compression force:* A force acting on a body tending to compress the body. (Pushing action.)
  b. *Shear force:* A force acting on a body which tends to slide one portion of the body against the other portion of the body. (Sliding action.)
  c. *Tension force:* A force acting on a body tending to elongate the body. (Pulling action.)
  d. *Torsion force:* A force acting on a body which tends to twist the body.

Foundation — The substructure which supports a building or other structure.

Framed Opening — Frame work (headers and jambs) and flashing which surround an opening in the wall or roof of a building; usually for field installed accessories such as overhead doors or powered roof exhausters.

Framing — The primary and secondary structural members (columns, rafters, girts, purlins, brace rods, etc.) which go together to made up the skeleton of a structure to which the covering can be applied.

Framing Drawings — Plans and erection instructions which identify all individual parts in sufficient detail to permit the proper erection and installation of all parts of the metal building system furnished by the seller (also known as Erection Drawings).

Gable — A triangular portion of the endwall of a building directly under the sloping roof and above the eave line.

Gable Roof — A ridged roof that terminates in gables.

Galvanized — Coated with zinc for corrosion resistance.

Girder — A main horizontal or near horizontal structural member that supports vertical loads. It may consist of several pieces.

Girt — A secondary horizontal structural member attached to sidewall or endwall columns to which wall covering is attached and supported horizontally.

Glaze or Glazing — The process of installing glass in windows and doors.

Grade — The term used when referring to the ground elevation around a building.

Grade Beam — A concrete beam around the perimeter of a building carrying an exterior wall.

Grout — A mixture of cement, sand, and water used to fill cracks and cavities. Often used under base plates or leveling plates to obtain uniform bearing surfaces.

Gutter — A channel member installed at the eave of the roof for the purpose of carrying water from the roof to the drains or downspouts.

Gusset Plate — A steel plate used to reinforce or connect structural elements.

"H" Section — A steel member with an H cross section.

Haunch — The deepened portion of a column or rafter, designed to accommodate the higher bending moments at such points. (Usually occurs at connection of column and rafter.)

Header — A horizontal framing structural member over a door, window, or other framed opening.

High Strength Bolts — Any bolt made from steel having a tensile strength in excess of 100,000 pounds per square inch (690 MPa). Some examples are ASTM A-325, A-449, A-490.

High Strength Steel — Structural steel having a yield strength in excess of 36,000 pounds per square inch (250 MPa).

Hinged Base — See Pin Connection.

Hip Roof — A roof which rises by inclined planes from all four sides of building. The line where two adjacent sloping sides of a roof meet is called the *Hip*.

Hoist — A mechanical lifting device usually attached to a trolley which travels along a bridge, monorail, or jib crane. May be chain or electric operated.

Hood (Door) — The metal flashing used over exterior slide door track along the full length of the door header to protect the tracks from weather and to conceal them for aesthetic purposes.

Hot-Rolled Shapes — Steel sections (angles, channels, I-beams, etc.) which are formed by rolling mills while the steel is in a semi-molten state.

ICBO — International Conference of Building Officials.

Impact Load — An assumed dynamic load resulting from the motion of machinery, elevators, craneways, vehicles, and other similar moving forces.

Impact Wrench — An electric or pneumatic device used to tighten nuts on bolts.

Insulation — Any material used in building construction to reduce heat transfer.

Internal Pressure — Pressure inside a building which is a function of wind velocity, and number and location of openings.

Jack Beam — A beam used to support another beam or truss and eliminate a column support.

Jack Truss — A truss used to support another truss or beam and eliminate a column support.

Jib Crane — A cantilevered boom or horizontal beam with hoist and trolley. This lifting machine may pick up loads in all or part of a circle around the column to which it is attached.

Jig — A device used to hold pieces of material in a certain position during fabrication.

Kick-Out (Elbow) — (Turn-Out) A lower downspout section used to direct water away from a wall.

Kip — A unit of measure equal to 1,000 pounds (4.4 kN).

Knee — The connecting area of a column and rafter of a structural frame such as a rigid frame.

Knee Brace — A diagonal brace designed to resist horizontal loads usually from wind or moving equipment. This member normally has the lower end connected to a column and the upper end connected to an eave strut.

Lean-To — A structure such as a shed, having only one slope or pitch and depending upon another structure for partial support.

Leveling Plate — A steel plate used on top of a foundation or other support on which a structural column can rest.

Liner Panel — A panel applied as an interior finish.

Live Load — Live load means all loads, including snow, exerted on a roof except dead, wind, and lateral loads.

Load Indicator Washer — A washer for high strength bolts in which pre-tension load can be measured as a function of amount of compression on raised portions of the washer.

Loads — Anything that causes a force to be exerted on a structural member. Examples of different types are:

a. Dead Load
b. Impact Load
c. Roof Live Load
d. Seismic Load
e. Wind Load
f. Crane Load
g. Collateral Load
h. Auxiliary Load

Louver — An opening provided with fixed or movable, slanted fins to allow flow of air.

Masonry — Anything constructed of materials such as bricks, concrete blocks, ceramic blocks, and concrete.

Mastic — Caulking or sealant normally used in sealing roof panel laps.

MBDA — Metal Building Dealers Association.

MBMA — Metal Building Manufacturers Association.

Moment — The tendency of a force to cause rotation about a point or axis.

Moment Connection — A connection between two members which transfers the moment from one side of the connection to the other side, and maintains under application of load the same angle between the connected members that exist prior to the loading. Also, a connection that maintains continuity.

Moment of Inertia — A physical property of a member, which helps define strength and deflection characteristics.

Monolithic Construction — A method of pouring concrete grade beam and floor slab together to form the building foundation without forming and pouring each separately.

Monorail — A single rail support for a material handling system. Normally a standard hot-rolled I-beam.

Multi-Gable Building — Buildings consisting of more than one gable across the width of the building.

Multi-Span Building — Buildings consisting of more than one span across the width of the building. Multiple gable buildings and single gable buildings with interior posts are examples.

Newton — SI unit of measure for force (N).

Panels — See Roof Covering or Wall Covering.

Parapet — That portion of the vertical wall of a building which extends above the roof line at the intersection of the wall and roof.

Pascal — SI unit of measure for force per unit area (N/m^2).

Peak — The uppermost point of a gable.

Peak Sign — A sign attached to the peak of the building at the endwall showing the building manufacturer.

Piece Mark — A number given to each separate part of the building for erection identification. Also called mark number and part number.

Pier — A concrete structure designed to transfer load from the base of a column to a footing.

Pig Spout — A sheet metal flashing designed to direct the flow of water out through the face of the gutter rather than through a downspout.

Pilaster — A reinforced or enlarged portion of a masonry wall to provide support for roof loads or lateral loads on the wall.

Pin Connection — In structural analysis; a member connection to a foundation; another member or structure is designed in such a way that free rotation is assumed.

Plastic Design — A design concept based on multiplying the actual loads by a suitable load factor and using the yield stress as the maximum stress in any member.

Plastic Roof or Wall Panels — Panels used to admit light. They are normally of the same configuration as the metal roof or wall panels, and installed in the same plane.

Ponding — The gathering of water at low or irregular areas on a roof.

Pop Rivet — See Blind Rivet.

Portal Frame — A rigid frame structure so designed that it offers rigidity and stability in its plane. It is used to resist longitudinal loads where diagonal bracing is not permitted. (Also "Wind Bent.")

Post (End Post) — A secondary column at the end of a building to support the girts and in a beam-and-column endwall frame, to additionally support the rafter.

Pre-Painted Coil — Coil steel which receives a paint coating prior to the forming operation.

Press Brake — A machine used in cold-forming metal sheet or strip into desired cross sections.

Prestressed Concrete — Concrete in which the reinforcing cables, wires, or rods in the concrete are tensioned before there is load on the member, holding the concrete in compression for greater strength.

Primary Members — The main load carrying members of a structural system, including the columns, endwall posts, rafters, or other main support members.

Primer Paint — This is the initial coat of paint applied in the shop to the structural framing of a building for protection against the elements during shipping and erection.

Prismatic Beam — A beam having both flanges parallel about its longitudinal axis.

Purlin — A secondary horizontal structural member attached to the primary frame which transfers the roof loads from the roof covering to the primary members.

Rafter — A primary beam supporting the roof system.

Rails (Door) — The horizontal stiffening members of framed and paneled doors.

Rake — The intersection of the plane of the roof and the plane of the gable. (As opposed to endwalls meeting hip roofs.)

Rake Angle — Angle fastened to purlins at rake for attachment of endwall panels.

Rake Trim — A flashing designed to close the opening between the roof and endwall panels.

Reactions — The resisting forces at the column bases of a frame, holding the frame in equilibrium under a given loading condition.

Reinforcing Steel — The steel placed in concrete to help carry the tension, compression, and shear stresses.

Ridge — Highest point on the roof of the building which describes a horizontal line running the length of the building.

Ridge Cap — A transition of the roofing materials along the ridge of a roof. Sometimes called ridge roll or ridge flashing.

Rigid Connection — See Moment Connection.

Rigid Frame — A structural frame consisting of members joined together with rigid (or moment) connections so as to render the frame stable with respect to imposed loads, without the need for bracing in its plane.

Roof Covering — The exposed exterior roof skin consisting of panels or sheets, attachments, and joint sealants.

Roof Overhang — A roof extension beyond the endwall/sidewall of a building.

Roof Pitch — Ratio of rise to total width.

Roof Slope — The angle that a roof surface makes with the horizontal. Usually expressed in units of vertical rise to 12 units of horizontal run.

Rolling Doors — Doors that are supported on wheels which run on a track.

Sag Rod — A tension member used to limit the deflection of a girt or purlin in the direction of the weak axis.

Sag Strap or Sag Angle — See Sag Rod.

Sandwich Panel — A panel assembly used as covering; consists of an insulating core material with inner and outer skins.

SBC — Standard Building Code. (See SBCCI.)

SBCCI — Southern Building Code Congress International, Inc.

Screeding — The process of striking off the excess concrete to bring the top surface of the concrete to proper finish and elevation.

Sealant — Any material which is used to close up cracks or joints to protect against leaks.

Secondary Members — Members which carry loads to the primary members. In metal building systems, this term includes purlins, girts, struts, diagonal bracing, wind bents, flange, and knee braces, headers, jambs, sag members, and other miscellaneous framing.

Section Modulus — A physical property of a structural member. It is used in design and basically describes the bending strength of a member.

Sectional Overhead Doors — Doors constructed in horizontally hinged sections. They are equipped with springs, tracks, counter balancers, and other hardware which roll the sections into an overhead position, clear of the opening.

Seismic Load — Seismic Load is the assumed lateral load acting in any horizontal direction on the structural system due to the action of earthquakes.

Self-Drilling Screw — A fastener which combines the functions of drilling and tapping. It is used for attaching panels to purlins and girts.

Self-Tapping Screw — A fastener which taps its own threads in a predrilled hole. It is for attaching panels to purlins and girts and for connecting trim and flashing.

Shear — The force tending to make two contacting parts slide upon each other in opposite directions parallel to their plane of contact.

Shear Diaphragms — See Diaphragm.

Sheet Groove (Reglet) — A notch or block out formed along the outside edge of the foundation to provide support for the wall panels and serve as a closure along their bottom edge.

Shim — A piece of steel used to level base plates or square beams.

Shipping List — A list that enumerates by part number or description each piece of material or assembly to be shipped. Also called tally sheet and bill of materials.

Shoulder Bolt — A fastener used to attach wall and roof paneling to the structural frame. It consists of a large diameter shank and a small diameter stud. The shank provides support for the panel rib.

Shot Pin — A device for fastening items by the utilization of a patented device which uses a powdered charge to imbed the item in the concrete and/or steel.

SI — The international symbol for the metric unit used by the United States (Le Systeme International d'Unites).

Side Lap Fastener — A fastener used to connect panels together at the side lap.

Sill — The bottom horizontal framing member of an opening such as a window or door.

Sill Angle — See Base Angle.

Simple Span — The term used in structural analysis to describe a support condition for a beam, girt, purlin, etc., which offers no resistance to rotation at the supports.

Single Slope — A sloping roof with one surface. The slope is from one wall to the opposite wall of rectangular building.

Single Span — A building or structural member without intermediate support.

Siphon Break — A small groove to arrest the capillary action of two adjacent surfaces.

Slide Door — A single or double leaf door which opens horizontally by means of overhead trolleys.

Snow Load — A load imposed on buildings or other structures due to snowfall.

Soffit — The underside covering of any exterior portion of a metal building system.

Soil Pressure — The load per unit area a structure will exert through its foundation on the soil.

Spall — A chip or fragment of concrete which has chipped, weathered, or otherwise broken from the main mass of concrete.

Span — The distance between supports of beams, girders, or trusses.

Specifications — A statement of particulars of a given job, as to size of building, quality, and performance of men and materials to be used, and the terms of the contract. The most common specification found in the metal building systems industry is the "Recommended Guide Specifications for Metal Building Systems" published by the Metal Building Manufacturers Association.

Skylight — A roof accessory to admit light, normally mounted on a curbed, framed opening.

Splice — A connection in a structural member.

Square — The term used for an area of 100 square feet (9.29 M^2).

Stainless Steel — An alloy of steel which contains a high percentage of chromium. Also may contain nickel or copper. Has excellent resistance to corrosion.

Stiffener — A member used to strengthen a plate against lateral or local buckling. Usually a flat bar welded perpendicular to the longitudinal axis of the member. Large concentrated loads, such as crane loads, usually require stiffeners at the point of connection.

Stiffener Lip — A short extension of material at an angle to the flange of cold formed structural members, which adds strength to the member.

Stiles — The vertical side members of framed and paneled doors.

Strain — A change in length per unit length. It is the deformation of a body that is acted upon by forces.

Stress — A measure of the load on a structural member in terms of force per unit area (kips per sq. in.) (MPa).

Structural Steel Members — Load carrying members. May be hot-rolled sections, cold formed shapes, or built-up shapes.

Strut — A brace fitted into a frame work to resist forces parallel to its length.

Stud — A vertical wall member to which exterior or interior covering or collateral material may be attached. May be either load bearing or non-load bearing.

Suction — A partial vacuum resulting from wind loads on a building which cause a load in the outward direction.

Tapered Member — A built-up plate member consisting of flanges welded to a variable depth web.

Temperature Reinforcing — Light-weight deformed steel rods or wire mesh placed in concrete to resist possible cracks from thermal expansion or contraction.

Tensile Strength — The longitudinal pulling stress a material can bear without tearing apart.

Thermal Block — A spacer of low thermal conductance material.

Thermal Conductance (C) — The rate of heat flow, in BTU's per hour, through a square foot of material or a combination of materials whose surfaces have a temperature differential of 1° F.

Thermal Conductivity (k) — The rate of heat flow, in BTU's per hour, through a square foot of material exactly one inch thick whose surfaces have a temperature differential of 1° F.

Thermal Resistance (R) — Resistance to heat flow. The reciprocal of conductance (C).

Thermal Transmittance (U) — The rate of heat flow per square foot under steady conditions from the air on the warm side of a barrier to the air on the cold side, for 1° F. of temperature difference between the two. $(BTU/Ft^2 - hr - 1°\ F.)$

Thrust — The horizontal component of a reaction.

Tie — A structural member that is loaded in tension.

Torque Wrench — A wrench containing an adjustable mechanism for measuring and controlling the amount of torque or turning force to be exerted—often used in tightening nuts or bolts.

Track — A metal way for wheeled components; specifically one or more lines of ways, with fastenings, ties, etc., for a craneway, monorail, or slide door.

Translucent Panels — See Plastic Roof or Wall Panels.

Tributary Area — The area which contributes load to a specific structural component.

Trim — The light gauge metal used in the finish of a building, especially around openings and at intersections of surfaces. Often referred to as flashing.

Truss — A structure made up of three or more members, with each member designed to carry a tension or compression force. The entire structure in turn acts as a beam.

Turn-of-the-Nut Method — A method for pre-tensioning high strength bolts. The nut is turned from the snug-tight position, corresponding to a few blows of an impact wrench or the full effort of a man using an ordinary spud wrench.

Turnout — See Kickout.

UBC — Uniform Building Code. (See ICBO.)

Uplift — Wind load on a building which causes a load in the upward direction. (See Suction.)

Valley Gutter — A channel used to carry off water from the "V" of roofs of multi-gabled buildings.

Ventilator — An accessory usually used on the roof that allows air to pass through.

Wainscot — Wall material used in the lower portion of a wall that is different from the material in the rest of the wall.

Wall Covering — The exterior wall skin consisting of panels or sheets and their attachments, trim fascia, and weather sealants.

Web — That portion of a structural member between the flanges.

Web Member — A secondary structural member interposed between the top and bottom chords of a truss.

Wind Bent — See Portal Frame.

Wind Column — A vertical member supporting a wall system designed to withstand horizontal wind loads.

Wind Load — A load caused by the wind blowing from any horizontal direction.

"Z" Section — A member cold formed from steel sheet in the shape of a block "Z".

4
Metal Building Systems

Systems Concept

The metal building systems industry has adopted a systems approach to the fabrication and erection of buildings. Frames, walls, roofs, as well as construction techniques, have been standardized in order to realize the advantages of mass production, resulting in less material, better quality control, and faster fabrication and erection.

For the manufacturer, standardization of systems is accompanied by use of computer capabilities in design, drafting, and fabrication. In the plant, it means less unproductive time spent in re-tooling or equipment set-up, stockpiling certain components, and transferring expensive field labor into the plant where costs are lower and control is better. For the contractor, it means being able to estimate the cost of a building for a prospective owner in a relatively short period of time with a high degree of accuracy.

In the field, standardization of systems permits faster erection with a minimum of on-site labor, due to the familiarity of repetitive parts and practices. Less time spent in erection means that the owner can occupy the building, and begin realizing a return on his investment much sooner than would have been possible in other types of construction.

The net result of the systems approach, both in the factory and in the field, is a high quality building which is economical, and can be erected in a relatively short period of time.

Structural Systems

The primary structural system of a metal building system is the frame that supports the roof, walls, and all externally applied loads. There are several different types of framing systems in use today. Putting aside minor individual differences between manufacturers, they can be categorized as follows:

1) Single span rigid frame, usually tapered.

2) Tapered beam with type II connections at the columns.

3) Continuous beam frame, post-and-beam.

4) Single span and continuous trusses.

5) Lean-to.

Most manufacturers have the capability to produce several or all of these types. The selection of the appropriate type is determined by a combination of economics, function, and usage. For a given space requirement, a manufacturer will be able to recommend the most economical framing system, although function may dictate the use of a less economical system. For example, a prospective owner may require a wide, column-free interior which would suggest the use of a rigid frame, even though a continuous post-and-beam system might be more economical. A metal building systems contractor will be able to identify the needs of the owner and, with the help of the manufacturer, recommend the appropriate framing system.

The framing systems listed previously are usually welded up from plate and bar stock having a yield strength of 50 ksi. The member depths, and the plate thickness are determined by computer analysis in order to make the most efficient use of material. By tapering structural members, the most material can be used at those sections where the bending moments are highest. Standard hot-rolled sections are generally not used.

The frames are fabricated with pre-punched splice plates for easy field bolting. There are two types of connections used: simple (hinged, pinned) and moment connections. A simple connection joins members but permits them to rotate relative to each other, and has only the capacity to transfer shear and axial force from one member to another. This is referred to as an AISC Type II connection. A moment connection joins two members in such a way that bending moment can be transferred from one to the other.

Typically, all connections between members in a rigid frame are moment connections, made with end plates. Secondary members, which frame in to the primary members at a right angle, are generally joined with simple connections, as are columns to foundations. Simple connections require less bolts, thinner plates, and thus are less expensive than moment connections.

Single Span Rigid Frame

A rigid frame is used when interior columns cannot be tolerated. Standard spans up to 120' are available but special requirements of up to 200' spans may be met with non-standard designs. Columns are usually tapered and girders may be straight, singly tapered, or multiply-tapered.

Tapered Beams

A tapered beam may be used for moderate clear spans. The columns in this type of frame are straight and the girder tapers to a maximum depth at mid-span. The lower flange of the girder is thus kept horizontal, which is advantageous for certain applications, while the top flange provides the necessary roof slope for drainage. The column-to-girder connection is designed to resist moments due to wind loads, but provide enough flexibility under live load to be considered, effectively, a simple connection.

Continuous Beam Frames

The continuous beam frame, or post-and-beam, is used in applications where interior columns are not objectionable. The interior columns will cause the girder size to be reduced, which makes this frame more economical than a clear span rigid frame. Exterior columns are generally tapered and interior columns are straight in this system. The girders are normally tapered.

Single Span and Continuous Trusses

The single span truss and continuous truss are similar in application to the tapered beam and continuous beam. The only difference is that the roof support is a truss rather than a girder.

Lean-to

Lean-to systems are "add on" items. They normally are designed for vertical loads only, and rely on an adjacent structure for lateral support. Tapered beams and straight columns are usually used.

Most of the above structural systems are easily modified to accept cranes, monorails or other materials handling equipment. For guidelines on crane applications, the reader is referred to the "Crane Design Manual," published by MBMA. Likewise, all structural systems can be designed for the addition of canopies and lean-tos, either as an extension of the roof line or at a level below the eave height.

Wall Systems

Wall systems usually consist of two components: the wall panel and the girt. The girts, cold formed "C" or "Z" sections, are attached to the columns of the primary frame, and support the wall panel against lateral loads. They may frame into the column webs, or be attached to the outer flange. Flush framing provides more usable building area. The panel and girt act in concert to resist pressure and suction on the system due to wind.

Wall systems are normally classified as either Field Assembled Systems or as Factory Assembled Systems.

Field Assembled Systems

Field Assembled Systems consist of an outer skin element, insulation, girts, and in some cases, an inner liner panel. The liner panel is used when it is desirable to protect the field installed insulation.

Specific advantages of field assembled wall panels include:

1) Rapid erection of panels.

2) Good cost competition with a large number of manufacturers and contractors being capable of erecting panels.

3) Panel replacement is quick and easy in the event of panel
   damage.

4) Openings for doors and windows can be created quickly
   and easily.

5) Panels are lightweight so that heavy equipment is not re-
   required for erection. Also large foundations and heavy
   spandrels are not required.

6) Acoustic surface treatment can be added easily to interior
   panel wall at reasonable cost.

Factory Assembled Panels

Factory Assembled Panels generally consist of interior liner
panels, exterior metal panels, and insulation. Panels providing
various insulating values are available from several manufacturers.
The particular advantages of these factory assembled panels are:

1) Panels are lightweight and require no heavy cranes for erection, no large foundations or heavy spandrels.

2) Panels have a hard surface interior liner.

3) Panel side lap fasteners are normally concealed producing
   a "clean" appearance.

4) Documented panel performance characteristics, determined
   by test, are usually available from reputable manufacturers.

Wall systems can be further classified as either "exposed fastener systems" or "concealed fastener systems,"with the former
usually being more economical.

Exposed Fastener Systems

Panels for exposed fastener systems vary in depth, and are
available in widths of two feet to four feet, and thickness ranges
from .0179″ to .0478″ in steel, and .024″ to .050″ in aluminum.
The most common wall panel thickness is .0179″. They are attached to "C" or "Z" girts with self-tapping screws, self-drilling
screws, or expanded fasteners, and joined to each other at their
sides and ends in lap joints.

There are several types of exposed fastener wall systems. The
original wall system from the Quonset hut days is still available,
and is called a "corrugated panel." This is clearly the most

economical wall system available. It is ½″ deep, and is available in standard widths from 30″ to 48″.

Today, the common type of exposed fastener wall system is the "profiled panel." Profiled panels range in depth from 1″ to 2″, are available in widths from 28″ to 40″, and have intricate and varied patterns and colors—which are more architecturally appealing than the "industrial look" of corrugated panels. The edge details of these panels also provide a more weather-tight side lap than the corrugated panel.

"Deep ribbed panels" are used when extra strength is needed. These panels are 3″ to 4½″ deep and are most commonly available in 12″ and 24″ widths. The extra depth makes 20 ft. spans between girts (with an applied 30 psf wind load) possible. Since these panels are stronger, they are manufactured in longer lengths which will reduce the number of pieces needed to construct a high wall.

Concealed Fastener Systems

Concealed Fastener Wall Systems are designed with edge joints that conceal the fasteners. These panels are also avilable in many different profiles and finishes that provide a pleasing architectural appearance.

Roof Systems

The roof system is made up of two components: purlins and roof panels. The purlins support the weight of the roof and any applied loads, and transfer these loads to the primary structural system. Two types of purlins in common use are cold formed steel "Z" or "C" sections and open web joists. The "Z" or "C" sections can have either a simple connection, or a moment connection where they meet and are attached to the frame, and can be used on spans of up to 30′. For spans greater than 30′, open web joists or deep "Z" or "C" sections may be used for purlins.

The roof panels are fabricated from light gauge steel, and fall into two general categories: lap seam roof and standing seam roof. The former has been used for a longer time period than the latter. The panels used for a lap seam roof are typically 1″ to 2″ deep and usually .020″ or .024″ (26 to 24 gauge) thick. They are connected to each other by lapping, as the name implies. A sealant is installed between the two panels at the side, and end laps and fasteners are used to secure them.

The selection of panel depth and thickness is affected by roof load, purlin spacing, and insurance considerations. The panel depth and thickness determine the strength of the panel. Given the roof loading and purlin spacing, the required panel strength can be calculated, and the appropriate panel can be selected. Oftentimes insurance regulations, by such companies as Factory Mutual, will require panel depth or thicknesses greater than the building codes will require. (See Chapter 13.)

The development of the standing seam roof was a major breakthrough in the design of metal roof systems. The system was first introduced in the late '60's, and today most manufacturers either offer it, or plan to provide it in the near future. The difference between the standing seam roof and lap seam roof lies in the manner in which two panels are joined to each other. The seam between two panels is made in the field with a tool that makes a cold formed weather-tight joint. (Note: some panels can be seamed without special tools.) The joint is made at the *top* of the panel. The standing seam roof is also unique in the manner in which it is attached to the purlins. The attachment is made with a clip concealed inside the seam. This clip secures the panel to the purlin and may allow the panel to move when experiencing thermal expansion or contraction.

The special characteristics of the standing seam roof produce a roof that is superior to built-up or exposed roof systems. A continuous single skin membrane results *after* the seam is made since through-the-roof fasteners have been eliminated. The elevated seam and single skin member provides a watertight system. The ability of the roof to experience unrestrained thermal movement eliminates damage to insulation and structure (caused by temperature effects which built-up roofs commonly experience). Thermal spacer blocks are placed between the panels and purlins in order to insure a consistent thermal barrier. Due to the superiority of the standing seam roof, most manufacturers are willing to offer considerably longer guarantees than those offered on lap seam roofs.

Accessories

In addition to frame, wall, and roof systems there are other components of a metal building system generally referred to as accessories. These include insulation, gutters, downspouts, roof ventilators, roof openings, interior liner panels, wall vents, wall openings, windows, pedestrian doors, overhead doors, canopies, skylights, fascia, and trim in general. Any number of these items are required to complete a metal building system. These individual components are also manufactured as integral units for the metal building system. When installed, they will be compatible in both design and appearance with the wall and roof systems that they penetrate.

Special Systems Applications

The majority of metal building systems in existence today can be classified as being modular in layout and typically one story high. There are, however, numerous systems that are exceptions to this general description. Multi-story buildings, circular buildings, heavy crane buildings, and airplane hangars are examples of projects that have used metal building systems successfully. The technology and experience to handle non-modular building configurations exists, and provides a large market for metal building systems to enter in the future.

5

General Design Principles

Design Loads

The first step in the design of a metal building system structure is to determine the safe loads which the structure must be able to support. The designer (architect, engineer, or metal building system contractor) relies on design manuals, building codes, manufacturers' specifications, and the owner to help him determine what loads the building must support. The following is a list of different loads typically encountered:

1) *Dead Load* — The weight of all permanent construction, such as floor, roof, framing, and covering members.

2) *Roof Live Load* — Superimposed loads exerted on a roof (e.g., construction loads, maintenance traffic).

3) *Roof Snow Load* — Including effects of drifting.

4) *Seismic Load* — The lateral load acting in any horizontal direction on the structural system due to the action of earthquakes.

5) *Wind Load* — The loads (horizontal and vertical) caused by wind blowing from any horizontal direction.

6) *Auxiliary Loads* — Specified dynamic live loads, other than the basic design loads which the building must safely withstand, such as cranes, material handling systems, and impact loads.

7) *Collateral Loads* — Specified additional dead loads other than the building dead load, such as sprinklers, mechanical systems, electrical systems, and ceilings.

The actual value of each one of these load types is referred to as the design load.

After the design loads have been determined, the designer must determine what combination of loads will produce the most critical effect upon the building. Building codes and experience determine these load combinations. Quite conservatively, it could be assumed that all the design loads would be applied to the structure at one time. However, the probability of an earthquake occurring simultaneously with a 90 mph wind and a three foot snowfall is extremely small and would result in a heavy, uneconomical structure. The following is a realistic combination of the basic loads:

The loads listed herein shall be considered to act in the following combinations, whichever produce the most unfavorable effects on the building or structural member concerned.[1] (D = Dead Load; RL = Roof Live Load; RS = Roof Snow Load; W = Wind Load; S = Seismic Load; A = Auxiliary Load.)

a. D + RL

b. D + RS

c. D + A

d. D + W (or S)

e. D + RS[2] + A

f. D + RS[3] + S

g. D + .5W (or S) + A

h. D + RS + .5W

i. D + .5 RS + W

Notes:

1. All combinations of loads shall include floor live loads where appropriate unless the inclusion of same results in lower stresses in the members under investigation.

2. Roof snow load (RS) in this combination shall be:

Zero when the design snow load is less than 13 psf;
.5RS when, 14 psf is less than the Design Snow Load, less than 31 psf;
.75RS when design now load is greater than 31 psf.

3. Roof snow load in this combination shall be:

Zero when design snow load is less than 31 psf;
.25RS when design snow load is greater than 31 psf.

The designer will apply these various load combinations to the building structure, and determine the forces exerted upon each member of the structure due to the application of the load. The process of finding the member forces caused by a certain loading is called analysis. The number of load combinations to be considered, and the complexity of performing analysis, has led to extensive use of the computer. The computer enables the designer to analyze many load combinations in a relatively short period of time. The accuracy and speed of the analysis permits more efficient use of materials to be made.

Metal Building Systems Manual

The MBMA has published a manual which applies specifically to low-rise metal building systems. The main objective of the manual is to compile and publish recommended design standards that, when incorporated into building specifications, will insure high quality metal building systems.

The first section of the manual recommends design practices to be followed when designing a metal building system. A majority of this section is devoted to defining and recommending minimum design loads for metal building systems. Wind, crane, and snow loads are especially well covered in this section. Formulas for calculating wind pressure and suction for various building geometries are given. Values of lateral, tractive, and impact loads for overhead cranes are listed. Also, methods to calculate the effect of drifting snow are given.

The remainder of the manual consists of recommended guide specifications for metal building systems, metal building systems nomenclature, and codes of standard practice. The purpose of these sections is to compile standard practices, specifications, and language used by metal building systems manufacturers and contractors in a single publication.

Site Planning

There is no single element that is as critical to the overall effectiveness of the utilization of a building operation than proper site planning. In a manual such as this, devoted to all aspects of the metal building systems industry, it is not possible to present a detailed treatise on site planning. Entire courses, in engineering and architectural schools, are developed toward such a goal. What can be done is to *summarize* key aspects of good site planning.

At the outset, a distinction must be made between site planning and site selection. The old adage that there are only three things important to proper site selection—"location, location, location"—may appropriately be mentioned here. Site selection is *the* key to the success of a project. Some of the factors that affect the *selection* of a site include:

Access to rail.

Access to highways.

Access to labor.

Expandability.

Good site drainage.

Good soils.

Proper *shape* of property.

Good on-site traffic.

Cost of land.

Access to utilities.

Access to suppliers.

Labor conditions.

Property tax considerations.

Income tax considerations.

Access to markets.

Economy of the area.

Availability of energy.

This book cannot possibly hope to develop definitive guide-lines on site selection. Many of the previously listed factors are, in fact, *intangibles* and cannot be evaluated in a quantitative form.

However, once a site has been selected and purchased, a second phase of site evaluation comes into play. This is the site planning phase where the optimum use of the site must be developed. All too often, many of the criteria previously listed as affecting site selection are redundant, due to the simple fact that the client *owns* the site. It may not be perfect. It may, in fact, be a bad site, which nonetheless is *the* site. There are some things that proper site planning can do to make the most of any site—good or bad.

1) *Consider expansion potential.* — Unless the site is totally occupied by building, think of how the building might be expanded. What about rail access? What about drainage or soil conditions? What about plant operations?

2) *Consider ingress-egress.* — Suppliers, customers, employ-ees, and shippers must have easy access to and from the site. Don't place curb openings too close to corners or where bad traffic conditions can occur. Consider rush hour traffic problems. Can customers find *and* get to the offices?

3) *Consider on-site traffic flow.* — Traffic on-site is often ignored. Cars and trucks must safely interact with people. Pedestrians should not be required to cross major truck traffic lanes. Where do trucks unload? Is a beautiful facility viewed by the passer-by as a line of semi-trailers? Should truck loading be covered? What about "turn-around" facili-ties on-site? Is trucking loaded on grade or are truck docks required? How are truck docks to be drained? What about ice problems in truck docks in cold climates? What about icicles and snow melt from roofs in cold climates? Are car and truck servicing and storage areas required? What about handicapped parking and access? Clearly one does not just "drop" a building on a site.

4) *Consider soil conditions.* — Many industrial facilities are large. On a large site, soil conditions can vary. It is possible

(since many desirable sites already have buildings) that one end of a site exhibits good soils while the other exhibits poor or marginal soils. If a structure has a basement, placing a building in an area of marginal soils may make sense, since foundations will be deeper than the depth to poor soils. A slab-on-grade structure might alter one's thinking on a location that has poor soil condition.

Therefore, site planning is an essential phase of the total design process. Good planning can turn a marginal site into a workable site. Poor planning can transform a good site into a disaster.

Building Layout

The building layout is a floor plan showing the entire area to be covered by the structure. For an industrial building, the relative loaction of offices, machinery, pits, truck wells, loading docks, doors, building columns, and traffic aisles are all things that should be shown on the layout. Elevations of equipment or machinery requiring headroom or access clearances should also be shown. The building layout provides a graphic representation of the owner's building requirements.*
Working with the owner and his layout, the contractor (sometimes the designer) will be able to determine what type, size, and shape building is required. The investment of time and money required to produce a good building layout will eliminate potential problems. For example, building column spacing is very closely related to door size, equipment layout, and office layout. Improperly placed columns can obstruct traffic, hinder production, and ruin office space.

A modular layout will usually result in the most economical building and refer to a regular, repeating column and framing plan. This will result in a building with many similar frames and pieces. This enables the manufacturer to maximize the production of components comprising the metal building system.

Selection of the Structural System

Based on the owner's needs, the contractor will be able to suggest the most economical structural system to do the job cor-

---

*For other commercial spaces, the specific layout is generally "owner specified" and varies with budget, operation, and basic use requirements.

rectly. Some of the factors affecting this decision are:

    Clear span requirement.

    Interior column spacing.

    Usage.

    Aesthetics.

    Future expansion.

    Often an owner requires a large open space for his operation. Exposition halls, recreational facilities, and factories are examples where this may be true. For these situations a frame without interior columns is required. Depending on the exact clear span needed, a rigid frame, tapered simple beam frame, or truss frame could be selected. The rigid frame has the greatest clear span capacity with clear spans up to 200 feet.

    Where interior columns *can* or *must* be tolerated for excessive spans, a continuous frame or continuous truss can be used. The spacing of frames will determine purlin and girt systems. Cold formed "Z" or "C" sections can usually span up to 30 feet. Bay spacings in excess of 30 feet will require wind columns to be installed to reduce the girt span, also requiring open web joists to be used for purlins. Jack beams or trusses and rafters can also be used when bay spacings exceed 30 feet.

    Sometimes the intended usage of a building will require a special structural system. Occasionally a manufacturer may recommend that a truss frame or continuous truss be used when heavy overhead cranes are required for structural reasons. The need to route utilities throughout a building may also dictate use of a truss frame or continuous truss, since the openings in a truss provide an excellent envelope to do such routing.

    Architectural needs may also *require* use of a particular system. For example, some owners may not be able to tolerate haunched columns protruding into office areas. In this case, a straight column would have to be used, or possibly a column in which the taper occurs on the exterior side of the column. A certain desired roof profile can also affect the selection of structural systems.

    It should be emphasized that one of the great advantages to the metal building system is its versatility. Expansion can be accomplished with relative ease in these structures. However, the need for future expansion should be considered when selecting the structural system. The building should be designed so that if expansion takes place, it can be accomplished with a minimum of structural modifications. Placement of diagonal X-bracing and endwall frame design to accommodate future expansion can greatly simplify the task. Adding a crane or removing bracing in the future without proper, prior planning and review could be serious.

Use of Computers

Modular design, mass production, and standardization of components have made it possible for computers to have a significant impact on the metal building systems industry. Computer analysis and design of structures by the manufacturers have enabled engineers to make the most efficient use of the available building materials. The increased accuracy produced by the computer has resulted in the use of less material without compromising safety. Prior to computer usage in analysis and design, designers were often forced to use approximate methods of analysis. These methods were not only time consuming, but were also inexact, forcing the design to be overly conservative.

The computer may also be used for drafting. The time consuming and expensive use of the drafter to produce working drawings can be replaced by computerized automated drafting systems. These systems get the design information to the manufacturing plant in less time with less expense than the traditional manual method.

Manufacturers also make use of computers for fabrication. Bills of material and material lists are prepared by computer. Automated welding machines and beam punches are computer controlled. The use of the computer has increased production, reduced fabrication time, and improved quality control.

6
Energy Considerations

Heat Transfer Concepts

Most building codes, including government and model codes, are requiring high standards for building designs relative to energy considerations. These high standards must be met, and yet include some compromise between such factors as enforcement considerations, initial cost, operating cost, and ease of design.

This chapter is devoted to an examination of the energy-related aspects of the metal building systems industry. This includes an introduction to heat transfer concepts, followed by a discussion of insulation characteristics.

Heat is transferred through walls and roofs, and is either gained or lost, depending on whether a building is experiencing summer or winter external environmental conditions. During the winter, it is desirable to keep heat in a structure, and to minimize heat loss. The reverse is true in the summer.

Along with the heat transfer concept, one must also consider the humidity problems. In many operational situations, inside air will have higher humidity than outside air. A vapor pressure difference is created whereby moisture tends to flow outward. In cold weather climates, such moisture migration may create a problem due to condensation. If the inside temperature is 70° F. and the outside temperature is 10° F., somewhere in the wall or roof construction, the dew point temperature will occur. At this temperature, water vapor condenses. This condensation may cause corrosion, leaking, and other similar problems. Also, moisture may condense *in* the insulation making the insulating value virtually worthless, as well as causing damage (sometimes permanent) to the insulation.

Several solutions to the condensation problem are available but not all are practical. Clearly, if no interior moisture is available, then no moisture movement will take place, and no condensation will occur. Such an environment is intolerable to humans—in fact, we intentionally humidify interior spaces for the comfort of occupants.

A more practical solution is to develop a vapor barrier to prevent moisture migration. Anyone living in a cold climate is familiar with condensation of water on cold window glass. The dew point exists on the glass surface. Condensation on the interior surface of the wall is rare however. The dew point is usually not on the wall surface, but somewhere in the wall construction. Paint and other vapor barriers (plastic sheets, foil backed insulation, etc.) prevent (or at least reduce) moisture movement through the wall, and condensation is minimized or eliminated. The existence of a vapor barrier is critical to the prevention of the condensation (corrosion) problem. Obviously, for unheated or unhumidified interior spaces, the moisture problem does not exist.

Prior to discussing the various methods for insulating metal buildings and pertinent advantages relative thereto, a discussion of the modern building code requirements is appropriately given at this stage. Most codes, in a positive attempt to save energy, will require the meeting of certain standards. Such standards should be realistic, yet easily used by designers, and also easily enforceable by code officials. Development of such a standard, which satisfies all of the preceding, is a difficult task at best.

At this point, most model codes and many states have adopted Standard 90-75 of ASHRAE (American Society of Heating, Refrigerating and Air Conditioning Engineers). This standard is based on what are technically referred to as "steady-state conditions," which means constant temperatures inside and out. This is not completely accurate in terms of "real world" conditions, but it does represent a reasonable compromise between absolute accuracy and reasonable ease of calculation.

A more accurate analysis could be made using *actual* weather conditions coupled with *actual* building use conditions. Such an analysis is possible with the application of computer modeling. This "dynamic" analysis is permitted by most codes, but is costly and not justifiable on many projects. In order to make 90-75 "reasonable" for the designer, certain simplistic assumptions must be made, or conversely, certain real life phenomena must be ignored.

One such area is the so-called "mass effect" or thermal lag. This concept will be discussed in a subsequent section of this chapter. At this point it may only be appropriate to state that the "mass effect" has been interpreted differently by the various facets of the industry.

Since ASHRAE 90-75 is so critical to the entire energy concept, it is reasonable that a brief synopsis of its provisions be included in this book. There is a danger in including such a summary, because code provisions like 90-75 will change. It is hoped that the general overview presented here will not be affected by editorial or minor technical change.

ASHRAE 90-75 evolved as a result of the energy crisis. The philosophy of 90-75 is to develop *performance* standards for energy applications in buildings. The document specifies both minimum performance criteria, as well as specific design criteria.

Specifically, *minimum* requirements are established for the thermal design of all elements of the building envelope (i.e. walls, roofs, and fenestration). In that context, 90-75 specifies use of established procedures for selecting HVAC systems based on the actual weather *history*. Further, it mandates that design conditions for heating and cooling are not the same.

Other specific requirements relating to HVAC systems include:

- Specific ventilation rates
- Criteria for selecting controls
- Use of energy recovery systems

- Insulation of ducts and piping
- Cooling with outside air

A major section of 90-75 is devoted to HVAC equipment manufacturers. The thrust is toward improved efficiency of equipment and improvement in the quality of operation and maintenance manuals relative to energy considerations.

Service water heating is also given major emphasis. Requirements are given relative to use of minimum recovery systems and storage tank and piping insulation.

Electrical energy and lighting are also given major treatment. Standards for distribution are given. All equipment greater than 15 watts must meet certain efficiency requirements. Service voltages are specified to be maintained at optimum levels. Lighting requirements include providing an adequate number of switches, and as much natural light as is consistent with good insulation practice for walls and roofs. Individual metering of building tenants is encouraged—to put everyone on a pay-for-what-*you*-use basis. Finally, the document encourages innovation, and use of non-depleting energy sources, such as wind and solar.

Insulation

In general, heat transfer (heat gain or heat loss) is principally affected by the amount of insulation extant in walls or roof. The effectiveness of this insulation is measured by the resistance, or "R value." The greater the "R" value, the greater the resistance to heat gain or heat loss (i.e., a reduction in heat transfer). By increasing the "R" value, significant reductions in energy costs can be achieved. The requirements of use for a particular space will dictate the energy consumption and corresponding required insulation.

Literature on energy and heat transfer concepts may refer to a "U" value as well as an "R" value. Effectively, the "U" value is the reciprocal of the "R" value. "U" is a measure of heat transfer rate and carries units of BTU/hr/square foot/degree F. The lower the "U" value the better the insulating quality (lower heat flow). "U" values are always given for an entire system (i.e., the *combined* effect of all the insulating values of the components of a wall or roof system), whereas "R" values normally are used when referring to a property of a "layer," or component of a system.

It is possible to calculate "U" values for engineering materials using thermal properties of components in a given system. The following are examples of how "U" values can be calculated for two different wall systems.

Insulated Metal Wall

Component	"R" Value
Outside air film	0.17
Metal panel	—
4" insulation (Fiberglass)	14.8
Liner panel	—
Inside air film	0.67

Total "R" = 15.64

$$\text{"U" value for system} = \frac{1}{R} = \frac{1}{15.64} = .063$$

Insulated Brick and Block Wall

Outside air film	0.17
Brick	0.44
1½" rigid insulation	7.50
Block	1.11
½" drywall	0.10
Inside air film	0.67

Total "R" = 9.99

$$\text{"U"} = \frac{1}{R} = \frac{1}{9.99} = 0.10$$

Mechanical engineers routinely do this when designing HVAC systems. However, "U" values can also be determined by testing. Test values are more realistic, as they included effects of compressed insulation and heat leaks at fasteners. Table 6-1 illustrates "U" values for the commonly used metal roof insulation system, fiberglass blankets.

There are various methods whereby insulation can be incorporated in a metal building system and several types of insulating materials which are in common use. Since many states are incorporating minimum insulation ("U" value) requirements, it is essential to be aware of the various possible types of insulation systems available.

Tested "U" Values — BTU/sq. ft./hr./° F.

Insulation Thickness*	Theoretical Uncompressed	One Fastener/Ft. Compressed on 5′ Purlin Spacing	Two Fasteners/Ft. Compressed on 5′ Purlin Spacing
1½″	.18	.20	.21
2″	.14	.17	.19
3″	.10	.13	.15
4″	.07	.12	.14

*.6 lb./cu. ft. vinyl-faced glass fiber insulation

Table 6-1. Results of MBMA/TIMA Hot-Box Tests on Typical Metal Building System Roof and Wall Constructions.

In this chapter numerous methods for insulating metal building systems are illustrated, some of which carry patents. These methods are neither endorsed nor, in fact, recommended, but are presented to acquaint the reader with the various systems that exist. Of particular note is the fact that vapor barriers are not shown for several of the systems.

Insulation which has been used in metal building systems includes: blanket, rigid, sprayed-on and foamed-in-place. The blanket type is usually a foil or paper-backed product. The rigid insulation may be one of many types of "boards" including plastics and pressed fibers. These boards have varying degrees of insulating capabilities and must be examined carefully in that regard. Some rigid insulation products are "pre-finished" with vinyl such that they may serve as the inside surface in the building. Also some types of rigid insulation are "closed cell" plastics which offer excellent resistance to passage of water and water vapor. Other porous types will act like "sponges" if they become exposed to water. There are two types of spray-on insulation that have been used in metal building systems.

Cellulose is applied as chopped cellulose fibers (recycled newsprint) and a liquid binder. It is inexpensive, but care must be taken to insure that the binder used will not react with the metal surfaces. In a humid atmosphere, it has been known to absorb moisture and cause a corrosion problem.

Foam plastic has also been used in spray applications on the interior of buildings, but *exposed* foam is almost universally prohibited in current building codes because of fire and smoke problems. Foam plastics are currently being used in spray-on applications to the exterior of existing roofs. Increased insulation and weather-tightness can be obtained in this manner. A membrane is required over the foam to protect it from ultra violet degradation. Foamed-in-place insulation (foam plastic) normally refers to building panels that are factory assembled units. Efficient insulated panels are produced by taking two formed faces and injecting the foam chemicals between the panels, and allowing the foam to fill the cavity. This results in a composite panel with the foam protected on each side by a metal face.

Finally, the various insulation materials in common use have differing fire performance characteristics. This performance is usually indicated by a fire hazard classification rating determined by a flame spread test. The rating would be indicated, for instance, by "Flame Spread — 25." These ratings are used solely to measure and describe the performance under controlled laboratory conditions. The numerical flame spread rating is not intended to reflect hazards presented under actual fire conditions. Careful consideration should be given to the selection of the insulation and to its proper installation and protection.

One of the common methods for insulation is the "Field Insulated Cladding System." Single-sheet, exposed-fastener panels are usually insulated with rolls of vinyl or foil-faced fiberglass. The insulation is attached to the outside of the structural frame and the panels are applied over it. Panel fasteners *penetrate* the insulation at girts or purlins, and as a result, the insulation becomes compressed—thereby reducing the overall thermal effectiveness of the panel. Figure 6-2 illustrates this condition. Figure 6-3 illustrates the results on the roof in winter. The compressing of insulation can significantly increase the "U" value.

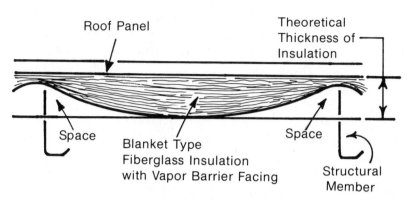

Roof Panel

Theoretical
Thickness of
Insulation

Space

Blanket Type
Fiberglass Insulation
with Vapor Barrier Facing

Space

Structural
Member

Figure 6-2.

Figure 6-3.

Another common method involves use of "Field Insulated Sandwich Panels." In this case, insulation (blanket or rigid) is placed between an exterior panel and an interior flat liner panel, which provides protection for the insulation not afforded in the "cladding system." The liner is applied to the exterior face of the structural system. Insulation is placed behind the girts which are attached to the liner panels. Exterior metal cladding is applied to complete the "sandwich." These exterior cladding panels can have either exposed or concealed fasteners, and subgirts are not always required in all systems, particularly when rigid insulation board is used. If the interior liner panels are not corrugated (i.e. have standing ribs), then girts are required to support the exterior panels.

A third common system of providing insulation is the "Pre-insulated Sandwich System," of which there are two types. In one case, the final result is similar to the field assembled panel, except that the insulation is applied to the liner panel prior to shipment to the site of construction. In the other case, the complete sandwich panel (liner, insulation, and exterior cladding) is factory assembled. There are some instances in which the prefabrication process eliminates the need for girts. Typical panels have a gasket edge detail to enable a simple field erection procedure.

A fourth method is the "Preinsulated Composite Panel." This is a completely factory assembled panel, normally utilizing foamed-in-place insulation. The use of plastic insulation can result in "U" values of as little as to .06 in a two inch panel thickness. These panels have prepared edges for easy field erection, often including factory applied sealants, which can eliminate field caulking. The insulation can act as a shear transfer mechanism to develop composite action and excellent panel rigidity, often eliminating rib stiffeners.

As stated, one of *the* significant problems associated with the insulated roof or wall panel is the potential for increase in "U" value as a result of compression of the insulation. This problem can be alleviated by placing the insulation *inside* the purlins or girts. Figure 6-4 illustrates this patented technique. Not only is the compressibility problem eliminated, but additional resistance to heat flow is developed as a result of the extra air space that is formed.

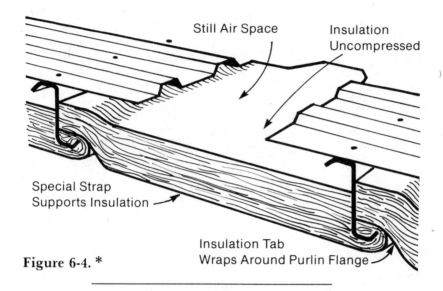

Figure 6-4. *

Another technique which can be employed to reduce heat transfer due to insulation compressibility is by use of "insulation blocks" as illustrated in Figure 6-5.

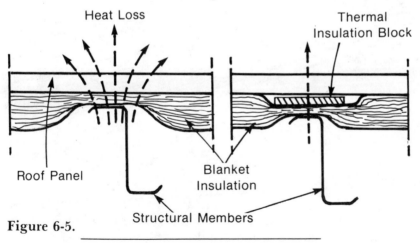

Figure 6-5.

Figure 6-6 illustrates a concept of installing insulation *between,* rather than over the purlins. Figure 6-7 illustrates the use of ceiling boards to create a support for batt insulation between purlins.

* **Source:** *CIS International* © 1979

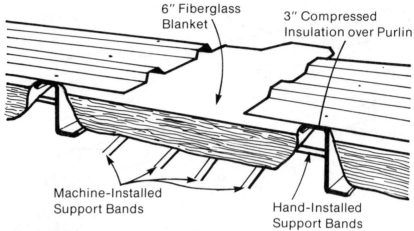

6" Fiberglass Blanket

3" Compressed Insulation over Purlin

Machine-Installed Support Bands

Hand-Installed Support Bands

Figure 6-6.*

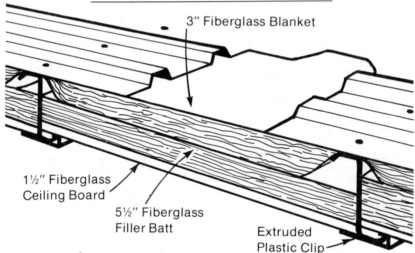

3" Fiberglass Blanket

1½" Fiberglass Ceiling Board

5½" Fiberglass Filler Batt

Extruded Plastic Clip

Figure 6-7.*

Due to the concern for energy savings existent today, many existing roof systems may be upgraded by adding insulation. It is possible that codes will require this to be done. Figures 6-8 and 6-9 illustrate two techniques for "re-roofing" an existing roof section. Generally, the concept is to add insulation over the existing metal deck, and then apply a new deck above this insulation using sub-purlins, clips, or spacers.

* Source: *CIS International* © 1979

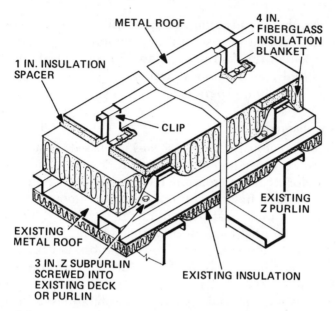

Figure 6-8.

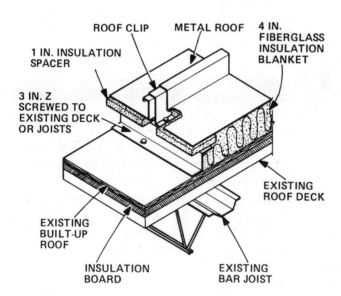

Figure 6-9.

One very obvious advantage of metal building systems, which the preceding discussion should make abundantly clear, is the ease with which these structures can be insulated—both at the time of initial construction as well as a part of a remodeling or energy upgrading program.

Mass Considerations

As stated previously, ASHRAE 90-75 is based on steady-state conditions (i.e. constant temperatures inside and outside). While this makes for ease of calculation, it is unrealistic in terms of what actually happens in a building. Computer models are now available to permit a "real" dynamic analysis of buildings. These models are permitted by most building codes.

One aspect of a "real world" consideration, not included in 90-75, is the so-called "mass effect." We have been aware for a long time that massive walls have a different heat transfer process. ASHRAE 90-75 permits taking advantage of the mass effect in the *cooling* cycle, using a concept called the Total Equivalent Temperature Difference (TETD). This enables a designer to make a more accurate evaluation of true heat gain to determine air conditioning loads. At present, no method is given for using mass in heat loss evaluation.

The concept of evaluating the mass effect was promulgated by the masonry industry starting in 1974. Extensive computer evaluations were made for representative wall thickness, and various areas of the country. In very basic form, the results of the study of the masonry industry consultants were the development of a correction factor (M factor) which may be divided into the required "U" value, to get a correct "U" value, which accounts for the effect of mass. Thus, a "thick" masonry wall may be permitted to have a higher "U" value than that required for a thinner wall. The "M" factor concept has been accepted by many local, state, and model codes. In regions where it has gained acceptance, massive walls do not have to meet as stringent requirements as light walls.

The metal building systems industry hired the Midwest Research Industry to explore the thermal performance of light and heavy buildings. Specifically, the effect of mass was evaluated for varying climatic conditions. The results of that study showed that mass does play a calculable role in controlling thermal performance.

It also showed that overall energy consumption was not greatly affected by mass alone, with only small percentage differences being observed. The study further showed that in colder climates where heating rather than cooling is dominant, insulation is the key factor in energy conservation. For structures in predominantly cooler environments, mass can *reduce* total energy consumption, provided that the building is unused during evenings and the delayed solar load can somehow be dissipated.

Other conclusions developed from the study were that the heat needed to reach design conditions, after setting back thermostats at night, was greater in massive wall buildings, thereby requiring larger HVAC equipment, or an earlier start-up. There is no question that both mass and insulation are important in terms of proper thermal performance of buildings. However, each building must be evaluated, and design based on its peculiar layout, operating schedule, thermal loads, external shading and climatic conditions. There is no way to develop a simple relation wherein "X" pounds of mass can replace "Y" inches of insulation.

There are numerous practical aspects of the "mass effect" that should be pointed out.

1) Due to the thin walls commonly used in metal building systems, little heat is stored in the wall system. Since these walls do not store heat, less *time* is required to achieve a comfortable room temperature. The HVAC system is used to heat or cool air and not walls.

2) The practical effect of mass is quite profound in many areas of the this country—more so than is obvious to the casual observer. The use of the "M" factor may reduce the effective "U" value for masonry walls to the extent that the requirements of ASHRAE 90-75 could be met by a masonry wall *without insulation*. The cost signifcance of such an effect is obvious.

3) Studies by the Midwest Research Institute (MRI) in 1976 indicate that only *slightly* higer peak heating and cooling loads exist for metal building systems than masonry build-

ings for either the heating or cooling cycle. These peaks are the highest loads on the "worst" day of the year, and do not indicate how many days such peak loads are reached in a year.

4) A better evaluation of thermal performance is *annual loads* (measured in BTU's) which relate to total energy demands. For identical "U" values, the annual heating load is slightly less for the masonry building for both one and three story buildings according to the MRI. Thus, mass *does* have a slight advantage relative to annual heating loads.

5) If building operations permit a reduction of building temperatures at night (lowering the thermostats), other significant developments were determined to exist per the MRI study. One significant point learned is that only the first ten degree setback generates significant savings. Lowering the thermostat 20 degrees results in only a slightly greater reduction in heating loads than for a ten degree setback. In the buildings studied, an energy saving of up to 28 percent was realized with a 10 degree setback. It is clear that nighttime setbacks do save energy. However, the MRI studies indicated that if nighttime setbacks are used, the light wall systems have, in fact, *smaller* total heating load requirements. It simply takes more energy to heat the massive walls during the recovery cycle. Figure 6-10 illustrates this concept.

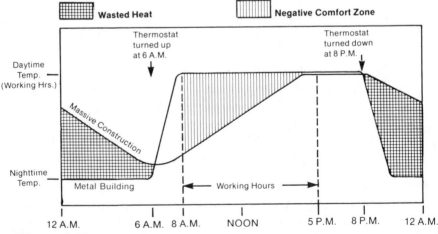

Figure 6-10.

Even with equal U-values, a metal building system has certain advantages over a masonry building. After a night setback of temperature, the light metal building system can be returned to a comfortable working temperature quickly the next morning. But the heavy mass building, because of its heat storage capacity, takes most of the working day to warm up.

Figures 6-11 through 6-15 (reprinted from an MBMA Publication, November 1978) graphically depict the results of the MRI study.

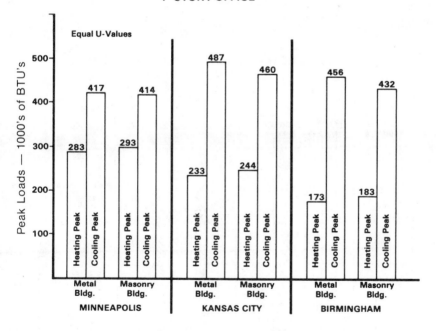

Table 6-11.

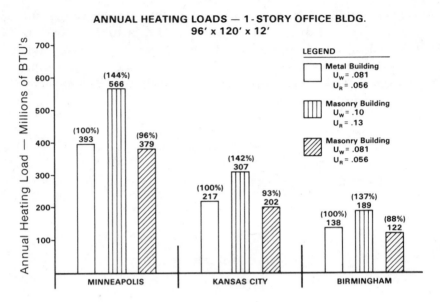

Table 6-12.

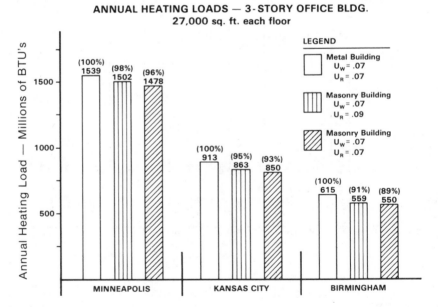

Table 6-13.

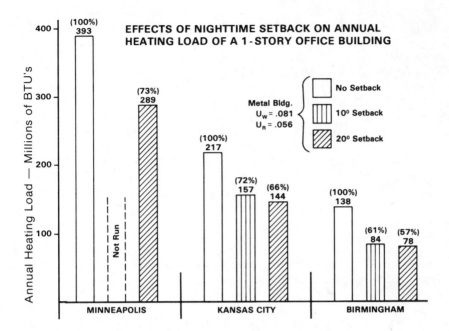

Table 6-14.

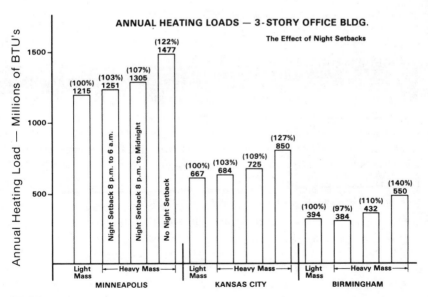

Table 6-15.

7
Life Cycle Costing

Building cost is probably *the* dominant factor relating to whether or not a particular project concept becomes a reality. Most investors evaluate the cost of construction, plus land costs, against the income which the completed project will generate, either in terms of rent or production benefits. In most cases, only *first* cost is evaluated. Life cycle costing (LCC) is simply the process whereby *all* costs (present and future) are included in the economic evaluation.

Life cycle costing would not be required if:

- All buildings had identical thermal characteristics
- Energy costs were not on the rise
- Energy sources were not diminishing
- The rate of inflation were zero
- Money did not have the power to earn money (interest)

The facts are that all of the above are not true. Two buildings with identical *first* costs may not necessarily have identical life cycle costs. Industrial engineers have been making life cycle cost studies for years. These studies have been called "engineering economy studies" and much can be learned from them.

The idea is simply to have some method by which all costs (present and future) can be evaluated in an economic study. Thus, such a total evaluation would include:

First Costs
- Land
- Site Work
- Fees and Permits
- Planning and Design
- Construction

Recurring Costs
- Maintenance and Repair
- Operation
- Decoration
- Heating
- Lighting
- Air Conditioning
- Costs of Sale
- Financing Costs

Unfortunately, one cannot simply add the cost of land purchase to the cost associated with selling the property 15 years later and call the sum a proper evaluation. If anyone has the option to receive $100 today or $100 in one year—today is clearly better. Why? Because the $100 could be invested and in one year could increase to perhaps $110 if 10 percent interest could be earned. Therefore $100 now is equivalent to $110 in one year if interest (the time value of money) is 10 percent.

Another way to evaluate the same situation is to recognize that future receipts are worth less than present receipts (the "bird in

the hand" concept). Therefore, any future receipts must be dis-
counted to properly evaluate their worth. This procedure routinely happens in financial matters. If a bond matures in 10 years
and will bring $1000 face value and pays 10 percent, and if each
year for 10 years the bond holder receives $100, and $1000 at
maturity and buys the bond for $1000, he will have earned exactly
10 percent on his investment. If he wants to earn more than 10
percent, he can do so only if he purchases the bond for less than
$1000. The bond price has then been discounted.

The concept of LCC procedures (or engineering economy
studies) revolves then around finding a means to include *all* costs
involved in any investment decision and to include them fairly—
recognizing the time value of money (i.e., future receipts are
worth less than present receipts).

Alternatives

Prior to describing methods for evaluating life cycle costs, it is
essential to point out that in making an economy study we are de-
ciding between alternatives. This may not seem to be a significant
point, but it is in fact the key to understanding what follows.

In any investment evaluation process, the investor decides
between various alternatives. For example:

a) Invest money in an almost risk free bank savings account
   with a "guaranteed" five percent return;

or

b) Invest in the stock market to gain a hoped-for 10 percent return;

or

c) Bury the money in the backyard.

The key here is that one always has the alternative to do nothing.

Many investment decisions are highly complex. The following
brief example will convey the complexity:

If money can be borrowed at a rate of 10 percent, which of the
following alternatives is the best investment?

Alternative "A"

First Cost $10,000

Annual Operating Costs $500/year

Resale Value $1,000

Life .... 10 years

Alternative "B"

First Cost $8,000

Annual Operating Costs $1,133.76/year

Resale Value $500

Life .... 20 years

Clearly, even an experienced investor cannot look at the preceding data and state which is the best alternative. (Are you surprised to learn that the two alternatives are identical? That is, they produce identical, uniform annual costs, including the effects of the time value of money at 10 percent.)

Methods of Analysis

There are several methods available by which life cycle costs can be properly evaluated. These include:

• Present Worth Method

• Annual Cost Method

• Rate of Return Method

Each of the above methods has certain advantages in certain types of economy studies. Generally, the annual cost method is most effective in industrial engineering applications. Various alternatives are compared on the basis of their uniform equivalent annual costs. For real estate investments, the present worth method is normally the most useful and informative. In this method, the present value of all future incomes and expenses, investments and sales, taxes and rebates, are calculated for all alternatives. The alternative with the lowest present worth will be the best investment.

Today, we are all aware of the energy crisis, and the general consensus that if we insulate, or add insulation in our homes, that we will save enough energy to get our investment back in a short period of time. This is an elementary form of a life cycle cost analysis.

In order to develop a life cycle cost analysis, it is essential to be able to use one of the proper evaluation methods. The Present Worth Method will be used in this book as the most appropriate method. In order to calculate the present worth (present value) of a future receipt or disbursement, four items of information are required:

- The interest (discount) rate, D
- The number of years until time of receipt (disbursement), n
- The amount of the receipt (disbursement), S
- A present worth (discount) factor, P

The present worth of a future receipt (or disbursement) can be evaluated from the following equation:

$$P = S \left(\frac{1}{(1+D)^n} \right)$$

The term in parentheses is known as the *single payment* present worth factor.

Certain investments can result in a *series* of savings or cost reductions. The present value of *each* yearly saving can be calculated using the previous equation. This is a time consuming process. Fortunately, a simple relation exists to evaluate the present worth of a series of receipts (or disbursements). For a *uniform* annual value, R:

$$P = R \left(\frac{(1+D)^n - 1}{D(1+D)^n} \right)$$

The term in parentheses is known as the *series* present worth factor.

Both the "series" and "single payment" factors involve calculation of exponential expressions. Not all readers may be capable of dealing with the required mathematics. Fortunately, tables are available which list these present worth factors for various terms and discount factors. Tables are presented here for an interest rate of 10 percent.

10 Percent Discount Factors

Term (years)	Single Payment Present Worth Factor (PWF)	Series Present Worth Factor (pwf)
1	.909091	.909091
2	.826446	1.735537
3	.751315	2.486852
4	.683031	3.169865
5	.620921	3.790787
6	.564474	4.355261
7	.513158	4.868419
8	.466507	5.334926
9	.424098	5.759024
10	.385543	6.144567
15	.239392	7.606080
20	.148644	8.513564
25	.092296	9.077040
30	.057309	9.426914
35	.035584	9.644159
40	.022095	9.779051
45	.013719	9.862808
50	.008519	9.914814

To illustrate the use of the Tables, the following examples are offered. All are obviously for a 10 percent discount (interest) rate.

Example 1

What is the present worth of $10,000 to be received in 15 years?

P = S (PWF)

P = $10,000 (.239392) = $2,393.92

This means if you value money at 10 percent, accepting $2,393.92 *now* is the same as receiving $10,000 in 15 years.

Example 2

What investment now can be made which will justify a cost savings of $500 per year for seven years?

P = R (PWF)

P = $500 (4.868419) = $2,434.21

Thus, if you had invested $2,434.21 now and had received returns of $500 per year for seven years, you would have made 10 percent on your investment.

The concept of "funds being available for 10 percent" deserves comment. If funds are not being borrowed, how can the concept of 10 percent interest be valid? The answer is that by making an investment, the opportunity to earn 10 percent elsewhere is now lost. Therefore, *all* life cycle cost evaluations must be made at whatever interest rate is appropriate. In some cases this will be the "cost" of borrowing. In other evaluations, it will be the "interest lost" by making *this* investment and not some other.

This chapter cannot hope to treat all aspects of life cycle costing. To do this properly one must include such complex topics as:

Effects of Inflation

Tax Considerations

- Depreciation
- Tax Credits
- Capital Gains
- Recapture

Evaluation of Intangibles

Financing Considerations

Cost Projection Concepts

To make a complete and thorough life cycle cost analysis, all of the above are involved. To make a "simplified" LCC analysis (i.e., to leave out some of the more complex aspects) may produce misleading and erroneous results. What is intended here is to make the reader aware that a first cost is *not* a valid basis on which to evaluate alternatives. Certainly it is important, but (just as with the concept of adding insulation) spending more money initially to develop a more energy efficient building may reduce life cycle costs, and may actually (in the long run) prove to be a cheaper (better) investment.

Simplified Methods

In addition to the three classical engineering economy methods listed previously as appropriate for LCC evaluations, there are other procedures which the reader may encounter that deserve mention in this chapter. They each have some merit, although it is the opinion of the authors that the present worth method is, in fact, *the* preferred method for most evaluations. It is possible to misuse many so-called simplified methods and to get absolutely wrong conclusions from them.

One such simplified method is the so-called "Pay Back Period" method. The Pay Back Period is defined as that period over which savings, or return from an investment, will totally pay back the invested funds. The procedure is as follows:

1) Calculate the net annual savings (AS) resulting from the investment. This may be a reduced electric bill, or similar saving in energy costs.

2) Divide this into the amount of the investment or first cost, (FC).

3) The payback period (PP) is the quotient, i.e.:

$$PP = \frac{FC}{AS}$$

If such an investment is paid back in, say four years, and has an expected life of 20 years or more, one might conclude that a rate of return of ¼ or 25 percent had been earned. The authors have heard this logic being used in a number of instances. It is erroneous. The concept of a pay back period is fine, and cannot be debated, since it is a defined term. But to argue that since an investment is paid back in four years it has resulted in a 25 percent rate of return, is not valid. This method does not deal with the concept of discount. Examine the two following situations:

Case I

Initial Investment $1,000
Savings Year #1 . . . . -$0-
Savings Year #2 . . . . -$0-
Savings Year #3 . . . . -$0-
Savings Year #4 . . . . $1,000
Total savings — $1,000 in four years.

Case II

Initial Investment..................... $1,000

Savings Each Year $250

Pay back period — four years.

Hopefully it is clear to the reader that while the pay back periods of both cases are identical, the fact that the investor receives his investment sooner in Case II makes it superior. Anyone would prefer to have a loan paid back using the repayment schedule of II rather than I. Thus pay back period is not a measure of rate of return. It is a *rough* evaluation of the general nature of an investment, *and no more.*

Another simplified method which is often encountered is the "Return on Investment"(ROI) concept. Like the pay back period, it has merit, can be misleading, and is not exact. The method involves calculating the return on investment (ROI) as follows:

1) Calculate the yearly depreciation (DC) of the investment

$$DC = \frac{FC}{n}$$

where "n" is the expected "life" of the investment.

2) Calculate the ROI from:

$$ROI(\%) = \frac{AS-DC}{FC} \times 100$$

If the investment of Case II has an expected useful life of 10 years then:

$$DC = \frac{\$1,000}{10} = \$100/year$$

$$ROI = \frac{\$250-100}{1,000} \times 100 = 15\%$$

Clearly this is different than the 25% rate that the pay back period approach suggested. While it is still not correct, it is a *measure* of the value of the investment. If the ROI were 30% or more, even though the 30% may not be strictly valid, the fact that the ROI is that high makes the concept worth studying in greater detail.

Thus, the only valid LCC methods will involve the time value of money concepts. The reader should be aware that the detailed study of investment decision-making is normally handled in graduate level courses in engineering and business schools. Therefore, it will not be logical to present a complex (realistic) example of a *valid* LCC study here. Even if one were presented, variations in the laws from state to state, and changes in Federal tax laws would make it invalid in most areas subsequent to the first printing of this book.

In summary, LCC is a proper and valid method by which building investments can be compared. LCC, when properly done, evaluates *total* project costs, including those due to energy. The LCC concept is included in this chapter, since *extra* first cost expenditures for one system (which result in energy savings) may result in a lower *overall* cost than a "cheaper" first cost structure with high energy consumption. Once an investor is exposed to this concept, it may be necessary to retain consultants to actually make the LCC study.

Also, the reader is cautioned to beware of simplistic methods to evaluate investments. Methods such as "pay back period" and "ROI" may be used to get a "feel" for which way to go, but only a full-fledged LCC study which includes all appropriate variables, including taxes, can be counted upon to give valid results.

Intangibles

Finally, the reader is cautioned that even the most experienced investment analyst consultant, who might be retained to make an LCC study, will be making assumptions. LCC involves estimating future cost reductions, energy expenditures, tax consequences, etc. For most of us the "crystal ball" is hazy *at best*. Therefore, the results of any LCC study can be expected to be no better than the assumptions upon which it is based. How accurately a consultant can estimate such things as:

cost of energy,

tax rates,

tax law changes,

operation costs,

labor rates,

inflation,

changes in interest (cost of money),

life of a piece of equipment,

will, in large measure, determine the value of the LCC study.

However, to make investment decisions *without* such a study, no matter how crude it may be, is much more likely to be in error. Since computer programs are available to accomplish LCC studies, various studies can be made in which high, low, and "most likely" costs are used in the analysis. Thus, results can be generated which would portray the most likely, most optimistic, and most pessimistic results of an investment strategy. If even under the worst set of future events, an investment still yields an "adequate" return, then that makes it likely to be successful. And if an LCC study leads to the conclusion that each of several alternatives will result in about the same overall life cycle cost, then the decision would be made on the basis of intangibles which include such factors as:

- When can the contractor start?
- Is one contractor more experienced than another?
- Is the contractor your brother-in-law?
- Can a past favor be repaid?
- Are you "partial" to one material or brand over another?

It is *possible* that a good decision can be made based on such intangibles. It is highly unlikely!

8
Foundation Design

In developing this book, there was some debate and hesitancy among the authors as to how heavily the subject of foundation design should be treated, if at all. Clearly, it has been our collective experience that more problems exist relative to foundations, than any other single aspect of the entire system, and that remedies are often expensive when problems do occur. Moreover, the intended readership of this book is broad, and will include many for whom what is included here will be the *only* exposure to a complete, yet basic treatment of the subject. As a result, this chapter is longer and more detailed than others. It is felt that the potential overall benefit to the industry makes this effort worthwhile, and in fact, required.

General Characteristics of Soils

To introduce the topic, soil may be described as a combination of solid particles (usually inorganic, but sometimes organic, such as peat), water, and air. The characteristics of a soil in terms of its engineering value, is highly dependent on the nature of the soil particles, the size of the particles, and the relative amounts of particles, air, and water in the soil make-up.

Soil Particle Sizes

Engineers have classified soil based primarily on particle sizes, since it is this parameter that has the most dominant effect on soil engineering properties. Soil sizes are determined by using sieves for the coarser particles, and by sedimentation for the finer particles.

For our purposes here, we may use the following terminology:

Classification	Size
Silts and Clays	Passes a No. 200 mesh sieve*
Fine Sand	Passes a No. 40 sieve Retained on a No. 200 sieve
Coarse Sand	Passes a No. 4 sieve Retained on a No. 10 sieve
Fine Gravel	Passes a ¾" sieve Retained on a No. 4 sieve
Coarse Gravel	Passes a 3" sieve Retained on a ¾" sieve
Cobbles	Coarser than 3"

*A sieve with 200 openings per inch.

Distinguishing between silts and clays is not based on size. The general difference relates to the plasticity of the material. Clays are much more plastic (moldable) than silts. Most soils do not exist in the ground in a pure state (i.e., fine sand, silt, etc.), but in combinations such as silty-clay, silty-sand, etc.

Soil Color

Color is an effective means to distinguish between layers in the soil stratification, or "soil profile." But color is of great importance to determine soil properties as well. Black and dark brown colors usually relate to the presence of organic materials. Red colors usually indicate the presence of iron and good drainage. Yellow soils also indicate iron, but poor drainage. Gray and blue soils indicate poor drainage soils, while white soils usually have high silica or lime contents.

Soil Profile

A vertical cross-section through the earth showing the various layers of soil encountered is called the soil profile. Unfortunately, soil strata are not of uniform thickness, so that soil profiles can vary greatly, even on a small lot.

Soil Water

The amount of water in a particular soil can have a profound effect on not only its engineering properties, but on construction operations as well. The amount of water in soil is always given as a percentage of its dry weight, and is determined by weighing the soil in its natural state, drying it out, and then weighing it again. Since the water content of natural soil can vary due to changes in temperature, ground water, climate condition, etc., it is important to know the variation in properties of soil as they relate to moisture content. There are several indices which are useful to relate soil properties to water content.

Liquid Limit

The Liquid Limit (LL) is the moisture content (%) at which a soil passes into the liquid state.

The test to determine the LL is a measure of the cohesion of the soil. Sandy soils have a low liquid limit and low cohesion. Silts and clays have higher liquid limits (40% to 60%). A high liquid limit soil usually indicates high clay content and low load carrying capacity. For example, a liquid limit of 50 shows that at the liquid state, a soil is two-thirds soil particles and one-third water.

Plastic Limit

The plastic limit (PL) is the moisture content (%) at which a soil changes to a plastic state. This is "defined" as having just enough moisture to be able to roll the soil into ⅛″ diameter threads. The plastic limit relates to the clay content, and is of no value for non-plastic soils.

Silts and clays have plastic limits, and the moisture contents of such soils relate to their bearing capacity. Soils with moisture contents below their PL have generally high bearing capacities. As the moisture content reaches and exceeds the PL, the bearing capacity decreases markedly.

Plasticity Index

The plasticity index (PI) is defined as the difference between the liquid and plastic limits (PI = LL - PL). The PI gives the range in moisture contents at which a soil is plastic. A small PI (e.g., 5) shows that only a small change in moisture will change the soil from a semi-solid to a liquid state. A large PI (e.g., 20) shows that a large change in moisture will not create a liquid state in the soil.

The LL, PL, and PI are referred to as the Atterberg limits, named for the inventor of the tests.

Density Relations

Soil particles have a specific gravity of about 2.65. Specific gravity is the term used to relate the weight of a material to the weight of water. Thus, a *solid* block of soil would weigh 2.65 x 62.4, or 165 pounds per cubic foot. Natural soils weigh in the range of 90 to 130 pounds per cubic foot (pcf). Obviously, natural soils must then have some spaces or voids. These voids may be filled with air or water (accounting for the variation from 90 to 130 pcf).

Moisture Content

This is the amount of moisture (m) in a soil sample expressed as a percentage of dry density.

$$m = \frac{W_W}{W_S} \times 100$$

The term is also referred to as natural moisture (NM). It is critical to know the NM of a soil. If, for example, a soil has a LL of 35 and a NM of 34, it means that a change of one percent moisture will cause the soil to change to the liquid state. Knowing the Atterberg limits without knowing the NM is quite useless.

Bearing Capacity and Settlement

In the design of any foundation system, whether it involves use of spread footings, piles, or caissons, there are three basic criteria that must be satisfied in order to have a safe, stable structure:

1) The structural element must be proportioned (area, depth)

and located in a suitable soil stratum, such that a soil "failure" does not result. Such a failure is more appropriately called a bearing capacity failure. Such a failure is obviously not tolerable, and foundations must be proportioned to have an ample factor of safety against such a failure.

2) The structural element must be proportioned and located so that total and differential settlements are kept below tolerable levels.

3) The structural element (footing, pile, caisson) must be structurally capable of supporting the loads. This implies adequate thickness and reinforcing. These parameters are determined from a complete structural design. The soil characteristics are not really relevant to this design phase.

Factor of Safety

Engineers and contractors are acquainted with the concept of a factor of safety. We want every element of a structure to have a *strength* which is larger than the load to which it is subjected. A structural element with a factor of safety of 1.0 is on the verge of collapse. In steel structures, we commonly use a factor of safety of 1.65, which is recommended by AISC. A similar factor of safety is used in the design of reinforced and prestressed concrete members.

When dealing with soil, a substantially larger factor of safety is commonly used. Unlike steel and concrete, which are manufactured, controlled, and tested to meet prescribed standards, soils are natural materials. Our knowledge of soils is considerably less than that of steel and concrete, and soil borings may be 50 or more feet apart on a given site. Soils are highly variable, and even on very uniform sites there may be pockets of poor, weak, and compressible materials.

Therefore it is common practice to apply a factor of safety of at least 3.0 in soil engineering work. We want to emphasize the words "at least." When for reasons of time, economics, or politics it is not possible to have a complete and thorough soil boring and laboratory analysis program, it is recommended that even larger factors of safety be used.

It is worth emphasizing that if a steel beam or column is overloaded, it can be strengthened with relative ease by the addition of cover plates, stiffeners, etc. at a comparatively low cost. If a footing is overloaded, the cost to strengthen it involves underpinning, bracket caissons, chemical intrusion, or other expensive remedies. Due to the variability of soil and the high cost of remedial work, a large factor of safety is recommended.

Mechanism of a Bearing Capacity Failure

A bearing capacity failure can occur under a shallow spread footing, a deep caisson, or a group of piles. For convenience, the case of a shallow footing will be described. If we load a footing to failure capacity, the failure mechanism will be as shown in Figure 8-1.

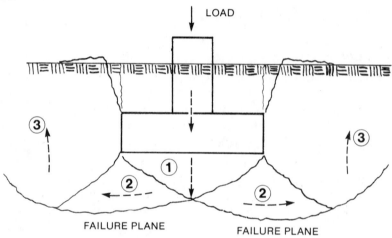

Figure 8-1.

As the column and footing move downward, a pyramid or cone-shaped volume of soil will move down with it. This is labeled "1" in Figure 8-1.

As this cone or "wedge" moves downward, the soil around it will move outward and upward with a failure plane occurring as shown. This material, labeled "2," continues to move out and forces zone "3" up until the surface of the ground actually bulges upwards, if the load is continually applied.

The "failure" of the soil is a shearing action along the "failure plane" shown. To cause failure, the footing load must be large enough to shear through the soil, and raise up the weight of the material in volume "3." There are a number of factors that affect this bearing capacity.

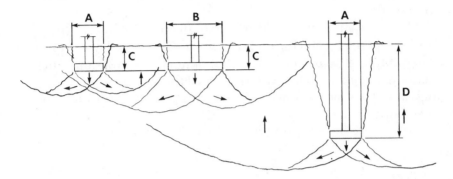

Figure 8-2.

Figure 8-2 shows the effect of foundation width. The "failure plane" is increased substantially due to the footing width being increased from "A" to "B." Retaining the original footing width "A," but increasing the depth from "C" to "D," also creates a major increase in the length of the failure plane. Since there is more failure plane that must be "sheared" before a failure can occur, the load to cause failure is much higher. As stated previously, the failure involves not only shearing along the failure plane, but also raising the weight of the soil in volume. It is clear from Figure 8-2 that as the footing or depth is increased, not only does the *length* of the failure plane increase but the weight of material in this volume increases also.

Thus the bearing capacity of a foundation is related to the following specific parameters:

1) Shear Strength of the Soil.

2) Footing Width.

3) Footing Depth.

4) Soil Weight.

5) Water Table.*

Of the above quantities, all but one relate to things which can be readily measured, selected, or weighed. The engineer selects

---

*The level of ground water affects the weight of the soil due to buoyancy. Soil under water is lighter due to the buoyant uplift.

the width and depth of the footing, the soil weight can be determined, and the level of the water table can be established by drilling a bore hole. Only the soil shear strength is not readily known.

The shear strength of soil is the single most important structural property. It can be *approximated* by field tests, but can only be established accurately with a laboratory test program. After many years of research, we have learned those particular properties and tests on soil which can be made to determine the shear strength.

The two basic soil properties which affect shear strength are:

$$c = \text{cohesion}$$

$$\Phi = \text{angle of internal friction}$$

These may be expressed in the equation to establish shear strength.

$$s = c + \sigma' \tan \Phi$$

where: $\sigma' =$ the intergranular pressure between the grains of soil. For soil with no cohesion, such as dry sand, this angle of internal friction is roughly equal to the angle of the pile created when gently dropped on a level surface. (Figure 8-3.)

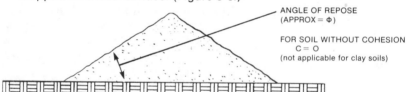

ANGLE OF REPOSE
(APPROX = Φ)

FOR SOIL WITHOUT COHESION
C = O
(not applicable for clay soils)

Figure 8-3.

Sandy soils generally have a value of ø of about 30 degrees, while clays in their natural state have a ø of from zero to ten degrees. For purposes of design, clays are usually assumed to have ø = 0. The "tan ø" is roughly equivalent to the "coefficient of friction" of the soil. The coefficient of friction times the normal force of "intergranular pressure" gives the friction portion of the shear strength.

The cohesion "c" is a measure of the "stickiness" of the soil grains. Sands have no cohesion, and derive all of their shear strength from friction. Clays, on the other hand, have practically no friction, and their shear strength comes from the cohesion. Soils found in a natural state derive shear strength from a combination of cohesion and friction. Moisture content has a very important effect on both "c" and "ø."

Mechanism of Settlements

Settlements of soils can result from a number of different causes, and will vary greatly, depending on a considerable number of parameters. Sandy (cohesionless) soils have entirely different settlement characteristics than clay (cohesive) soils.

Sandy soils settle primarily due to elastic compression of the grains. The settlements are generally small, usually occur immediately upon application of the load (during construction), and except for very loose sands,* are usually not a problem. Often, soils engineers will not bother to estimate settlements of foundations on sandy soils. For moderately loose sands, vibration can also cause settlement.

Clayey soils exhibit entirely different settlement behavior. Settlements occur slowly (sometimes many years pass before all of the settlement takes place), and settlements are often large. If a structure settles *uniformly,* even a two or three inch settlement may not cause building damage. This may however, create problems with sewers, and adjoining sidewalks and driveways.

Due to the non-uniformity of soils in nature, *non-uniform settlements can be expected.* These "differential" settlements, if large, can cause building damage, and cannot be tolerated. It is desirable to have minimum total settlements, as well as minimum differential settlements. The designer must have a means of calculating the settlements of clayey type soils.

Settlements in clay soils occur primarily because water in the soil-water mixture "leaves" the clay. When the water leaves, the pore spaces consolidate, and the soil can now occupy a smaller volume. This produces settlement or *consolidation.*

Water leaves the clay as a result of two possible external causes. First, and most commonly, water can be *squeezed* out of the clay as a result of foundation loads, or additional layers of fill, placed on a site. A second reason for water leaving the soil is that the water level drops, either naturally or as a result of pumping. Pumping (de-watering) in a construction operation can thus

---

*Very loose sands should not be used as a foundation unless very special study is made, or efforts are made to densify the soil.

result in settlement.

Soils have widely varying consolidation settlement characteristics. We may, for example, have a clay subjected to a heavy foundation load (causing a squeezing action). If a drainage layer exists (such as an underlying sand stratum), there will be a place for the water to go easily. If a clay layer has sand strata above and below, the process of consolidation will occur more rapidly due to the presence of two drainage layers, but the *total* settlement will be the same as if only one drainage layer existed. If no drainage layer is present, consolidation will still occur, but at a very slow rate—due to the difficulty of squeezing water through the tiny pore spaces in the clay.

Another important aspect of consolidation relates to the history of the soils in a particular area. There are many areas of the country in which glacial action has taken place. Generally this includes the northern states. In these areas, the heavy weight of the glaciers squeezed the water out of the clays thousands of years ago. Such soils are "pre-consolidated", and exhibit settlements of only about 10 to 20 percent of the settlements of "normally consolidated" clays. For example, soils in Wisconsin, Minnesota, and Michigan are almost all pre-consolidated.

Soil Borings and Field Testing

Soil borings are made for a number of reasons:

1) To locate all soil strata under the proposed structure.
2) To determine the water table elevation.
3) To determine the types of soils in each stratum.
4) To locate the extent of problem soils (such as peat and organic silt).
5) To obtain samples from which properties of soil can be determined in the laboratory.

Soil Boring Program

Unless soil characteristics are known prior to the construction of any building project, a well-thought-out soil boring program should be established. Based on the number of failures and lawsuits which have occurred, it is clear that the development of a soil boring program is the most consistently overlooked and ignored phase of the entire building construction program.

The cost of an adequate soil boring program is insignificant in terms of the potential problems which can result if borings are not taken. There is generally much controversy about the number and depth of borings which should be taken for a building project. The following set of rules should be taken as a minimum.

Minimum Soil Boring Program

1) Take one boring at each exterior corner of of the proposed building (minimum of four).

2) Take one boring near the center of the building.

3) One boring should be taken to a depth equal to the building width, or 100 feet, whichever is less.

4) All borings should be taken to a depth *below* any soft, weak, or organic soils.

Obviously, if shallow bedrock exists under the site, the borings should define the top surface to the rock stratum under the building. Also, if the borings taken show highly variable soils and stratification, additional borings are then required to establish critical areas or a soil profile.

A lawsuit recently resulted from a project in which three soil borings were taken. To "minimize" cost, borings were taken in the locations shown in Figure 8-4.

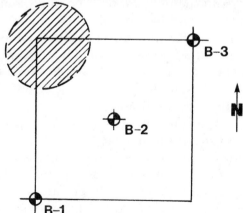

Figure 8-4. Boring Location Plan

Unfortunately, there was a "pocket" of organic soil, in the cross-hatched area shown, which, of course, was undetected. The northwest corner of the building settled about six inches.

Soil Boring Operations

There are several methods used for the making of soil borings. It is important to consider the soil boring operations in two distinct phases. The first phase is making the boring, which simply involves "making the hole." The second phase involves taking soil samples for testing.

The hole is made either by use of a flight auger, which literally drills a hole into the ground (about 6" diameter), or by use of a procedure called wash boring, in which a chopping bit is used to chop up the soil. Water is injected into the boring hole through a hole in the chopping bit. the soil and water mixture is then pumped out. It is important to remember that augering and wash boring methods only accomplish one thing—they make a hole in the ground.

In order to determine the engineering properties of soils, it is generally necessary to take soil samples for laboratory analysis. There are two commonly used techniques for taking these samples.

Split Spoon Sampling and the Standard Penetration Test

The type of sampler that is most commonly used to take soil samples is the "split spoon" sampler. The split spoon is a "pipe" with a threaded coupling at each end which can be split into two halves for easy removal of the soil. The split spoon is *driven* into the ground by use of a falling weight. The split spoon is about two inches in diameter, and the soil sample which is inside the spoon is a *disturbed* sample. The soil can be tested for certain properties, but the tests are limited.

Split spoon samples are usually taken at intervals of five feet, or wherever the soil stratification changes.

Since the split spoon is *driven* into the ground, soil engineers have learned through experience that the number of blows required to drive the split spoon into the ground is a measure of the density and bearing capacity of soil. This procedure is called the standard penetration test. The number of blows required to drive

the split spoon 12 inches into the ground using a 140 pound weight falling 30 inches is called the *"blow count,"* or "N" value. The blow count is a reasonable measure of the relative density and bearing capacity of granular (sandy) soils. It is of marginal, and perhaps questionable, use in determining the bearing capacity of cohesive (clayey) type soils. Table 8-5 gives a list of approximate allowable soil pressures for cohesive soils with varying blow counts. *These are very approximate, and are not recommended* except for unimportant structures or as a supplement to other analyses.

For Clayey Soils

Soil Consistency	N	Allowable Soil Pressure (lbs./sq. ft.)** Square Footings	Wall Footings
Very Soft*	0-2	0-600	0-400
Soft*	2-4	600-1200	400-900
Medium	4-8	1200-2400	900-1800
Stiff	8-16	2400-4800	1800-3600
Very Stiff	16-30	4800-9600	3600-7200
Hard	30 +	9600 +	7200 +

*Check settlement
**Approximate factor of safety of three

For *granular soils* equations have been developed to approximate the allowable soil pressure based on blow count — with an approximate safety factor of three.

For square footings

$$P_{allowable} = .7N^2BR_W + 2(100+N^2)DR_{W'}$$

For wall footings

$$P_{allowable} = N^2BR_W + 1.7(100+N^2)DR_{W'}$$

where:

N = Blow Count

B = Width of Footing

D = Depth of Footing

Rw and Rw' are factors varying from 0 to 1.0 which adjust for the location of the water table.

Table 8-5. Approximate Allowable Soil Pressures (based on blow count "N")

Shelby (Thin Wall) Tube Sampling

The standard penetration test and split spoon sampling are not reliable for clayey type soils. The only way to really establish the bearing capacity of clayey type soils is to make a laboratory test called the "unconfined compression test" to determine shear strength. In order to make the unconfined compression test, an undisturbed cylinder of soil is needed. This sample is obtained using thin wall tube sampling techniques.

In this process, a thin wall conduit is pushed (hydraulically) into the ground *rapidly*. The intent is to push the tube fast enough that the soil literally does not know that it has been disturbed. Shelby tube samples are usually taken at intervals, but sometimes continuously in clay soils.

The Shelby tubes are sealed in the field to prevent moisture loss and taken to the laboratory where the soil is pushed out (extruded) to obtain cylindrical samples for various tests.

Pocket Penetrometer

A commonly used approximate field test with which the reader should be acquainted involves the use of the calibrated spring, or pocket penetrometer. This is a device, about the size if a medium screwdriver, that is pushed *by hand* into clay type soils. It is not used for remote testing. A slide indicates the measure of difficulty required to push the penetrometer into the soil. The penetrometer is calibrated to read directly in tons per square foot. The more effort required to push the penetrometer into the soil, the higher the reading will result, and the higher the soil bearing capacity. The penetrometer gives a measure of the unconfined compression strength of the soil which is directly related to shear strength and bearing capacity for clayey type soils. The penetrometer should not be used for cohesionless (sandy) soils. The user may push the penetrometer into the soil by direct access to the soil (either by physically being in the excavation, or by having a large undisturbed sample into which the penetrometer may be pushed).

A number of tests made in the laboratory that are quite self-explanatory or have been discussed previously are tests for:

Unit Weight

    Grain Size

    Moisture Content

    Liquid Limit

    Plastic Limit

Other significant tests include:

    Unconfined Compression Test

    Consolidation Test

These tests are described in some detail due to their importance:

Unconfined Compression Test

This is a test of a small cylinder of soil, similar to the cylinder test used to obtain the strength of concrete. The failure of the cylinder is taken at that load which causes a shortening (strain) of 20 percent. This test is of *major importance* for determining the bearing capacity of clayey soils. For all practical significance, *the shear strengths of a clay may be accurately taken as one-half the unconfined compression strength* (q_u). The ultimate bearing capacity of a clay may be determined as follows:

$$P_{ult} = c \, N_c$$

where: cohesion = shear strength(s)

N_c = bearing capacity factor depending on size and depth of the footing.

The bearing capacity factor (N_c) does vary, but for a square footing, may conservatively be taken as 6.0. For a factor of safety of three, the allowable bearing pressure for a clay may be obtained as follows:

$$allow = \frac{P_{ult.}}{F.S.} = \frac{P_{ult.}}{3}$$

$$= \frac{c \, N_c}{3} = \frac{c(6)}{3} = 2c$$

Since (c) is $\frac{1}{2}$ of (q_u)

$$P_{allow} = 2c = \frac{2q_u}{2} = q_u$$

Thus, the allowable soil pressure in (psf) is equal to the

unconfined compression strength (q_u). Since the pocket penetrometer reading is an approximate measure of the unconfined compression strength, the pocket "pen" is often used to get approximate allowable soil pressures.

Consolidation Test

The mechanism of settlement of clayey soils was described previously. It was pointed out that settlement of clays results from squeezing water out of the clay. The consolidation test uses an undisturbed tube sample (preferably three inch diameter). The sample is placed in a cylinder with a porous plate above and below the sample. Load is applied to the sample in increments, and the water is squeezed out of the clay, similar to what happens in the ground.

A plot of void ratio (e), versus pressure (o ′), enables the determination of a term called the compression index (Cc), which is used in settlement calculations. The consolidation test should always be made for plastic clays of low shear strength. In areas where the soils are known to be preconsolidated, it may not be necessary to make this test. The consolidation test is difficult to make, and requires careful interpretation by an experienced soils engineer.

Engineering Properties of Soils

There are a number of important properties of soils with which every engineer and contractor should be familiar.

Properties of Granular Soils (Sands)

1) Immediate settlement.
2) Good backfill material.
3) Vibrations can cause settlement (loose sand).
4) Not a frost problem (unless sand is very fine).
5) Strength depends on density which is determined by standard penetration test (blow count).
6) Strength of loose sands can be improved by vibratory compaction.
7) High permeability—therefore dewaters or drains easily.

Properties of Cohesive Soils (Clays)

1) Soils are plastic (moldable) when moist.

2) Soils are compressible over a long period of time (consolidation) unless pre-consolidated.

3) May lose strength when wet or disturbed.

4) May develop large lateral pressures (poor backfill).

5) Highly impervious (good for earth dams).

6) Strength depends on cohesion which is generally measured by an unconfined compression test on an undisturbed sample.

7) Clays of high plasticity (LL over 40 percent) are poor foundation materials.

8) High capillarity of medium or soft clays make them susceptible to frost heave. (Not as serious as silts.)

9) Difficult to drain or dewater.

Properties of Silt (Laboratory Tests Are Mandatory)

1) Very fine particle sizes.

2) Low shear strength. (Glacial silty soils may not be weak.)

3) Low permeability.

4) Hard to compact.

5) Very susceptible to frost heaving.

6) If cohesive in nature, treat like a clay—if cohesion is less, treat like a fine sand.

7) Loess (wind blown silt) is very difficult to analyze and can be a major problem. An experienced soil engineer should be consulted for structures on loess.

Properties of Organic Soils (Peat, Organic Silt)

1) Soils are highly compressible. Settlements of two feet or more are common.

2) Blow counts may be high (deceptively), often high enough that it may appear that the soil is suitable as a foundation. These soils are *not* generally suitable for buildings.

3) Organic soils are often stable, and possess adequate bearing capacity, *as long as they are continuously submerged* (i.e., as long as the water table does not drop).

4) Organic soils can decompose if they are allowed to dry out or are alternately wet and dry.

5) It is possible to find soils with *small* amounts of organic materials in a generally suitable inorganic soil. Such soils may be acceptable for buildings, but should be carefully reviewed by an experienced soils engineer.

Compaction (Engineered Backfill)

There are many situations in which the surface soils on a site are of poor quality. If these poor soils do not extend to great depths, and if foundation loads are not exceptionally high, it may be economical to remove the poor surface soils and replace them with a compacted fill.

The fill materials used for compacted fill applications may be materials which are brought into the site, or they may simply be the *in situ* (in place) loose materials. Both granular and cohesive soils may be used as compacted fill materials.

There are various methods used to compact soils *in place*. The method used depends on the soil type and the particular site.

Flooding — Loose sands can be compacted in a limited way by flooding with water.

Vibration — Heavy vibratory rollers can compact a granular soil to a depth of several feet.

Vibroflotation — This is a commercial method involving a combination of vibration and jetting. Additional sands are brought in to fill in the voids created by the process.

Sand Drains — Vertical sand drains can be installed to accelerate the consolidation process of soft clays, (more drainage layers into which the water can be squeezed).

A man-made fill can be constructed to develop a soil with large bearing capacities and small settlements. A proper compaction procedure can increase shear strength and decrease compressibility. In order to determine the effectiveness of a field compaction operation, it is necessary to have a standard of comparison. The most widely used procedure to determine this standard is by use of the Proctor density test.

In the Proctor test, a sample of the proposed fill is brought to the laboratory. It is placed in a container at a particular moisture content, and a standard weight is dropped on the sample (in layers) to compact the material. The moisture content is changed several times, and the compaction process is repeated until the maximum density is achieved. The maximum density (at the optimum moisture content) is called the Proctor density. There are two Proctor tests, one called the Standard Proctor, and the other is called the Modified Proctor. The designer is cautioned to make sure which test is specified since different compaction procedures are used in each test.

In the Standard Procter test, the soil is compacted in a cylindrical mold having a volume of 1/30 cu. ft. The soil is placed in the mold in three layers, and tamped with a 5½ pound tamper falling 12 inches, with 25 blows per layer. The amount of compactive energy was established by testing, as approximately equal to that which is feasible to obtain in normal field compaction operations.

More recently, the U.S. Corps of Engineers decided that greater densities (e.g., under airport pavements, earth dams, earth embankments, etc.) might be required. For such projects heavier compaction equipment was needed. The Modified Proctor test was developed to check this higher level of compaction. In this test, the soil is placed in five layers, and is tamped with a 10 pound weight falling 18 inches, with 25 blows per layer. The Standard Proctor test is suitable for most building structures covered in this book.

For support of slabs on grade and moderate footing loads, engineers often specify that soils in the field be compacted to 95 percent of Modified Proctor density. This means that if the soils in the lab were compacted to 120 pcf, the soils in the field need only be compacted to .95 x 120 or 114 pcf. In order to determine whether or not this has been achieved, field density tests are made. After the soils have been compacted, a hole is dug and the material weighed. The hole is filled with a sand of known density. By weighing the amount of sand put into the hole, the volume of the hole can be computed. From this, the in-place density of the compacted fill can be calculated. It is thus possible to compact soils in the field to more than 100 percent of Proctor density, by doing a better job than is done in the standard test compaction procedure.

Since there is no well-defined relationship between Proctor density and bearing capacity, it is advisable to take standard soil borings on the site *after* the compaction has taken place, and then evaluate the borings, as if the soils were the natural soils for the site.

Compaction of man-made fill is accomplished by spreading fill materials at a moisture content near the optimum water content. If the soil brought in is too dry, moisture must be added; if too wet and slow drying, another source for materials should be found.

There are various types of equipment used in the compaction process. These include rollers, tampers, vibratory compactors, and earth moving equipment.

Rollers

   1) Smooth steel rollers are towed by a tractor and used to compact slag, rock, or coarse gravel.
   2) Pneumatic-tired rollers are also usually towed. Tires are inflated to about 100 psi, and the equipment is used for compacting granular soils.
   3) Sheepsfoot roller is a roller with a series of "footlike" projections used for compacting clay.
   4) grid roller is a roll covered with a "grid" of steel used for hard, lumpy clays.

Mechanical Tampers

   These tampers are for areas inaccessible to rollers, and where damage to nearby structures could occur.

Vibratory Compactors

   This is either a cylindrical roller, or pan type vibrator, which develops the compactive effort from a vibrating weight. The unit is excellent for compaction of granular soils.

Earth Moving Equipment

Trucks and tractors are commonly used for compaction, but are not generally satisfactory, primarily due to the fact that they do not develop a uniformly distributed compactive effort on the soil.

Specifying Compaction

Most engineers will write a "performance specification" for compaction work. This means that a specific density (such as 90 percent of Standard Proctor) will be specified. The fill material will be approved, and the contractor will then be permitted to use any method he wishes to develop the 90 percent density. Field density tests would be taken (generally by an independent testing lab) to make sure the compaction has been achieved. The specification may also state a limit on the maximum thickness of one layer of compaction (6-12 inches for clays and 18″ for granular soils).

Types of Foundation Systems and Foundation Behavior

It is a fundamental premise in all structural design, that all loads which act on a structure must eventually reach the foundations. These loads may be vertical loads, such as those caused by snow and structure weight. They may be horizontal, such as loads produced from wind, earth pressure, or seismic (earthquake) effects. They may also be a combination of vertical and horizontal load effects, causing tipping or rotation. The precise load combinations will vary from structure to structure, but they must be recognized, and taken into account in the design.

There are two broad classes of foundation systems:

A) Systems which support columns and are primarily transmitting *vertical* loads into the soil. (See Figure 8-6.)

B) Retaining systems which are constructed to support large *horizontal* forces. (See Figure 8-7.)

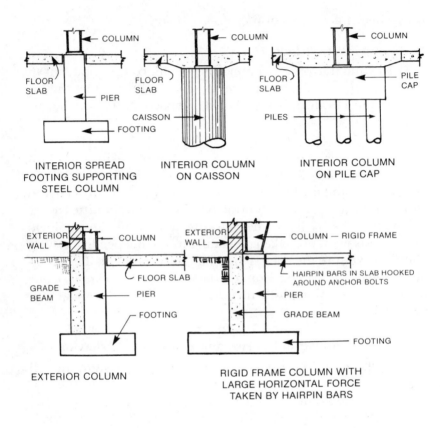

INTERIOR SPREAD
FOOTING SUPPORTING
STEEL COLUMN

INTERIOR COLUMN
ON CAISSON

INTERIOR COLUMN
ON PILE CAP

EXTERIOR COLUMN

RIGID FRAME COLUMN WITH
LARGE HORIZONTAL FORCE
TAKEN BY HAIRPIN BARS

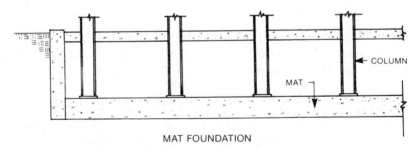

MAT FOUNDATION

Figure 8-6. Class (A) Systems

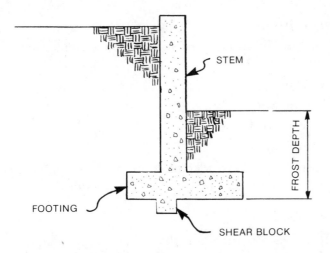

CANTILEVER RETAINING WALL

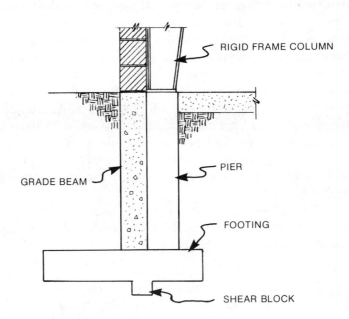

**RIGID FRAME COLUMN WITH
LARGE HORIZONTAL FORCE**

Figure 8-7. Class (B) Systems

Foundation Types

There are four basic types of foundation systems that will be discussed:

Spread Footings

Mat Foundations

Drilled Piers or Caissons

Pile Foundations

It is essential that the reader be familiar with the behavior and methods for sizing of these various foundations.

Spread Footings

Certainly, spread footings are the most common, and most economical, foundation system used. Very rarely would another type of foundation be used, if spread footings are adequate. The first step in the design of a spread footing is to determine that an adequate soil stratum exists on which the footing may be constructed. If the only "reasonable" stratum is 50 feet below ground surface, spread footings are not the answer.

Another factor to consider, in the decision on whether spread footings should be used, relates to the allowable soil pressure. Generally, soil pressures of 2000 pounds per square foot or more are considered adequate. If use of a pressure of 2000 psf results in footings which are 15 feet square, it may be more economical to use caissons or piles, or to excavate the soft upper materials and replace them with an engineered fill capable of developing a higher soil pressure.

There are other important considerations which must be made in selecting the depth of footing, which do not depend on allowable soil pressures. These include:

- Footings should be founded below disturbed ground (frost action, plantings, tree roots, etc.). Frost depth will vary with the location in the country. In the northernmost part of areas like Minnesota and Maine, frost depth is 4' 6" or 5', while in the South, frost depth really is not a consideration. In any area of the country, however, there is *always* some minimum depth to which soils have been disturbed by frost, vegetation, or construction activity, and footings should always be founded below such soils.

- Footings should be located below depths of excavation or adjacent structures (see Figure 8-8).
- Footings should be located below organic soils and topsoil.
- Footings should be located below sewer pipes, elevator pits, etc. to avoid being founded in backfill, as well as to avoid loading these other elements.

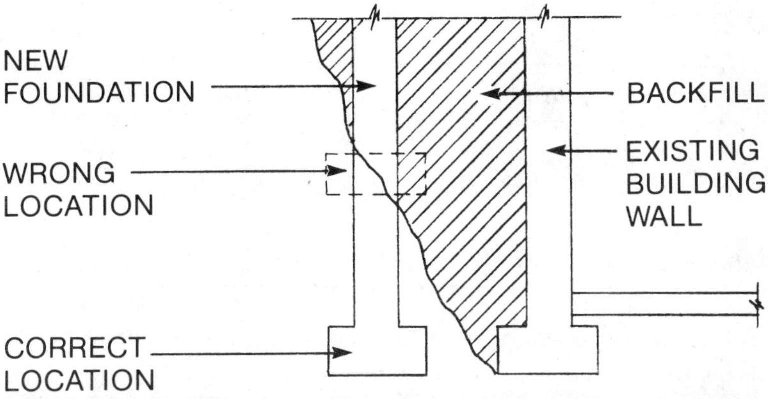

Figure 8-8. Footing Depth Consideration

Footings Subjected to Uplift

There is a special class of problem, wherein the structural configuration of a building is such, that some of the columns—under certain loading conditions—are actually subjected to an upward load. In such cases, it is necessary to "hold down" the column. This can be accomplished in several ways.

1) If the uplift is small, it may only be necessary to anchor the column into a footing which is heavier than the anticipated uplift. A minimum factor of safety of 1.5 is recommended if the uplift force is due to a wind.
2) If the uplift is much larger than the weight of a "reasonable" footing (say 10k), an alternate approach is used. In

order for a footing to be "lifted up," the soil on top of the footing must also be raised. Therefore, by lowering the footing a sufficient amount, a substantial increase in uplift resistance is developed.

Figure 8-9 illustrates the behavior of a footing subjected to an uplift load.

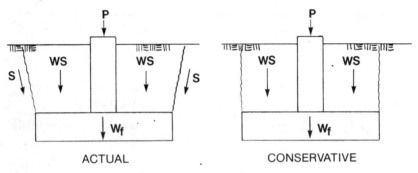

ACTUAL   CONSERVATIVE

Figure 8-9. Footing Subject to Uplift

The actual resistance to uplift comes from three sources. In order to move up, the columns must:

- Lift the footing weight (Wf)
- Lift the soil above the footing (Ws)
- Shear the soil around the perimeter of the soil volume actually raised. The shearing resistance is a function of the depth of the footing and the type of soil.

A conservative approach, which is often used by engineers, is to ignore the shearing resistance of the soil, and to ignore the fact that the failure plane will be inclined from the vertical. Figure 8-9 illustrates the actual and conservative approaches for this design problem. Since, in the development of this book, it was not possible to establish a specific depth of a footing, the footing tables for the zero moment case were developed in such a way that uplift forces will be resisted only by the footing weight. It will generally be economical in actual design conditions to drop the footing a sufficient distance, so that the weight of soil on top of the footing can be used in resisting uplift. Thus, P_{max} (uplift) should not exceed 2/3 (Wf) to provide a factor of safety of 1.5 against uplift.

Overturning

A common condition in the foundations encountered in building structures occurs when a large moment is applied to a footing which has a small axial load. It is entirely possible that an improperly designed footing could "tip over" under such a loading. The mechanism of overturning is illustrated in Figure 8-10.

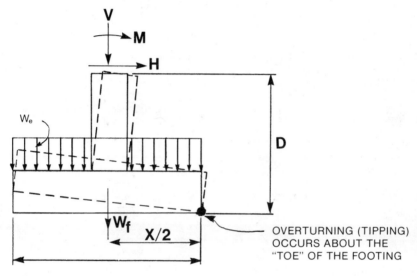

OVERTURNING (TIPPING) OCCURS ABOUT THE "TOE" OF THE FOOTING

Figure 8-10.

There are two ways in which a footing can be designed to resist the tendency to tip (including a proper factor of safety). One is to simply make the footing heavy enough that tipping cannot occur.

Another method, which will result in smaller footings, is to include the weight of soil and/or floor slab construction above the footing. Clearly, a footing will be much more difficult to tip if there is four or five feet of soil on top of it. Unfortunately, the designer cannot always be sure that the anticipated overburden will actually be there. It has been the experience of the authors, in a number of buildings, that the entire structure (roof, walls, etc.)

was completed, yet the backfilling had not been accomplished. (In one case, a plumber's strike precluded all underground plumbing installations.)

Effect of Adjacent Footings

A special situation that can occur in foundation design relates to the condition where a new footing is to be constructed adjacent to an existing structure. (This condition was discussed earlier in the chapter, relative to the danger of constructing a footing in a backfilled area.) The other "danger" relative to this condition is illustrated in Figure 8-11.

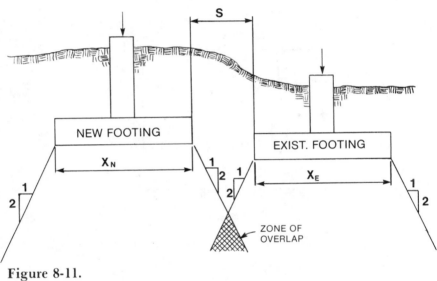

Figure 8-11.

If two footings are close enough to each other that the soil pressure diagrams "overlap" as shown, the soil in the overlap area is "stressed twice." For purposes of this book, and on the side of slight conservatism, the slope of the pressure diagram is taken as one horizontal to two vertical. Under this condition, if the soil pressure is 4000 psf, directly under a footing 10′ x 10′ in size, the soil pressure which exists 10′ below the footing bottom would be spread out over an area of 20′ x 20′, reducing the soil pressure at that level to 1000 psf. Unless the soils at that depth were very poor, there could be considerable overlap pressures existent without experiencing problems.

Mat or Raft Foundations

Occasionally, when soils are of low bearing capacity and extend to great depths, it is neither practical nor economical to use either caissons or piles. In such cases, a raft foundation may be feasible. A raft foundation is simply a large concrete slab which supports several building columns. In most structures, *all* columns and walls in a building would be supported on a single mat. A special case of a raft supporting only two columns is called a combined footing. The raft (and combined footing) will generally have very low soil pressures. A raft may also be used when individual spread footings get so large that they "almost touch."

When a building has a basement *and* a raft foundation, another special condition may exist. This is referred to as a "floating foundation." This term is used for the following reasons: A building which has a basement will have had ten or more feet of excavation. This ten feet of soil could weigh 1000-1300 pounds per square foot. If a building is placed on a mat, the soil pressures from the mat can be as much as 1000-1300 pounds per square foot, and the soil will have no more pressure than it did prior to the excavation. It is thus possible, with several levels below grade, to excavate soil which will exactly equal the weight of the building placed on the site. The building literally "floats" on the soil.

A mat foundation may be thought of as a large spread footing. The required size of the mat (area) is determined by adding all column loads, and dividing by the *net* allowable soil pressure. Normally, the general intent of the design is to develop a uniform soil pressure under the mat. This is accomplished by the following simple procedure:

- Find the location of the center of gravity of all column loads.
- Position the mat in such a way so as to locate the center of the mat coincidental with the center of gravity of the column loads.

The soil pressure under the mat will be uniform.

Drilled Piers or Caissons

A drilled pier or caisson may be looked on as a spread footing placed deep underground. These caissons are constructed using augers which can drill holes to six or more feet in diameter, and with bottom bells widened to 15 feet in diameter. (Not all contractors can construct the large sizes. A check should be made locally to determine equipment available.) The holes are filled with concrete (and some reinforcing).

Caissons are used when upper soil strata are soft and/or highly compressible (or organic), and are too thick to justify removal and replacement with compacted fill. Also, there are times when column loads are so large that a "relatively good" upper level soil (P_{allow} = 3000-4000 psf) will necessitate such large spread footings (20' x 20' or more), that it will often be more economical to use a caisson which extends to a deeper, higher quality stratum. Decisions to use caissons, based on the economics of foundation construction, should be made only by an experienced foundation engineer.

Caissons are ideally suited for use in cohesive soils. Such soils will "stand" vertically, enabling the caisson rig to rapidly drill and bell. In sandy soils the holes will tend to collapse. In order to prevent such collapse, the holes must be "cased" with a liner pipe or casing. This process works, but is expensive, and has one serious drawback. The liners are generally too costly to be left in place, and are withdrawn as concrete is being poured. If the liner is withdrawn too rapidly, there is a chance that the soils will collapse into the hole, resulting in a caisson with soil pockets (or worse, a caisson with several feet of soil where concrete should be.) Such problems have happened in a number of major buildings in this country. Careful field inspection is required to insure that this does not occur.

Caissons have high bearing capacity. Figure 8-2 illustrates the tremendous benefit a foundation receives from being placed *deep* in the ground. The bearing capacity is large due to the depth or "surcharge effect." The relations for ultimate bearing capacity of clay soils were previously described. For normal depth footings, the bearing capacity factor (Nc) was given as 6.0, and the allowable soil pressure resulted in being equal to q_u. For deep*

---

*For our purposes, a "deep" caisson is defined as having a depth equal to 2.0 or more times the bell diameter.

foundations, this bearing capacity factor increases from 6.0 to 9.0, and the allowable soil pressure takes corresponding increase. Therefore, for deep caissons founded on clay:

$$P_{allow} = 1.5\ q_u$$

In some soils it is not possible to bell the caisson bottom. A belled caisson is looked upon by most building officials as simply a deep footing. This will be true as long as the caisson bearing capacity is derived from the underlying soils. A "straight shaft caisson" without a bell will often have substantial load carrying capacity due to *friction* along the shaft. In this instance, the caisson is behaving more like a cast-in-place concrete friction pile. Building officials may require load tests for such cases. The authors have designed several projects with friction caissons, one of which was load tested in order to gain building code approval.

Caissons can be founded in sands as well as clays. One major problem, which occurs with caissons founded in sand, is the presence of ground water. In clay soils, there is relatively little water due to the impermeability of the clay. In free draining sands, water will readily fill the caisson hole, making drilling and placing concrete difficult. If a liner is used, and the water table outside the liner is high, there are two other potential problems. One is the collapse of the liner. This has happened on at least one major project, and received widespread publicity. The second is the danger of a "blowout." This happens when the soil at the bottom of the liner is blown out (up) from the water pressure below.

In summary, caissons are designed similar to spread footings, have high bearing capacity due to depth effects, and have a number of potential construction problems. It is the feeling of the authors that caissons are an economical and desirable foundation system requiring, however, careful field inspection.

Pile Foundations

Piles are commonly used when spread footings and caissons are either inappropriate or more expensive. Piles are considered as a foundation system when the soils, in which normal spread footings would be placed, are too soft or too compressible to support the footings. There is no simple rule which can be stated relative to the economy of piles versus caissons. In many instances, bids are taken on both systems. This is particularly true when use of caissons would require casing, adding to the expense of that system.

There are several different types of piles in common use. These include:

Timber

Steel H Piles

Steel Pipe Filled with Concrete

Cast-in-place Concrete

Precast Concrete

Each of these types have specific application in a wide variety of uses. Timber piles are the most common and generally the least expensive. They do, however, have limited load capacity and life. Recent studies have shown that old timber piles in certain areas of the country are showing signs of rotting. Of particular importance are areas of varying water table levels, and pollution of the ground water. When higher loads are required, several other types are suitable. The specific choice will depend upon soil conditions, economics, and availability. Another study of the National Bureau of Standards shows that steel H piles suffered no corrosion after many years, even in corrosive soils.

Piles are classified, not only by the materials of which they are made, but also by the method in which they develop load-carrying capability. Piles are classified as end bearing or friction piles. End bearing piles are those that are driven through soft materials, and develop load capacity by *bearing* on a hard, dense stratum, or by a short penetration into such a stratum. Friction piles develop their load capacity by friction with the soil, developed along the length of the pile. The frictional resistance, in large measure, comes from the displacement of the soil as the pile is driven. This displacement is accompanied by increased densification of the soil around the pile. In reality, most piles develop their capacity by a combination of both friction and end bearing.

This book does not present a comprehensive explanation of pile behavior. There are, however, certain basic considerations relative to pile foundations, that are important to all engineers and contractors.

1) Piles are commonly designated as 20 Ton, 30 Ton, etc. This capacity is rated by the lower of two values:

- The structural capacity of the pile material (e.g. wood, steel, etc.). Determining the structural capacity of a pile, based on the structural limitation of the pile itself, may be easily accomplished by use of available tables.

- *The capacity of the driven pile as limited by the soil strength.* This limitation relates to the combination of end bearing and friction between soil and pile. Determining the capacity of a pile, as limited by the soil, is not a simple nor accurate procedure. Most soil engineers do have methods available to make calculations for pile capacity, based on soil properties obtained from borings and lab tests. Most engineers recognize the limits of such a theoretical estimate.

2) One method in common use for determining pile capacity is the use of one of the pile driving formulae. The basis for this method is that a given pile hammer, driving piles of constant size and length into the same soil, will require the same energy to accomplish the driving. The number of blows of the hammer required to drive the pile the last 12 inches is recorded. Most pile driving formulae predict pile capacity on the basis of penetration and pile hammer energy characteristics. The most widely used of these formulae is the oldest. It is the Engineering-News Formula (often incorrectly called the Engineering News-Record Formula). Tests conducted by the Michigan Highway Department in which many pile driving formulae were studied and compared with the results of load tests on the piles, showed that the Engineering-News Formula, as modified by the correction factor proposed by the Michigan Highway Department, is the preferred pile driving formula. It is essential to emphasize that the pile driving formula is *at best* an approximate method. It can be used effectively in conjunction with load

tests. If pile capacity is based *only* on the pile driving formula, any design should be extremely conservative and used for low rise, lightly loaded structures.

3) A Pile Load Test is the most accurate, commonly used method for establishing the load-carrying capacity of a single pile. There is a standard accepted procedure for load testing a pile. It generally involves loading the pile by jacking against a heavy dead weight on a platform above the pile. The load is maintained for a period of time during which the settlement is measured. The load is then removed and the "rebound" of the pile is noted. A satisfactory pile test is one in which the pile carries the test load without exceeding settlement and rebound limits. Most codes require load tests which conform to ASTM Procedures (Designation D1194).

It is essential to recognize a major factor relative to the value of the pile load test. This factor is what is called "group effect." Piles are almost never used singly, but rather in groups. Unfortunately, the capacity of a group of piles, for example six piles, is not equal to six times the capacity of one pile. The driving of a pile affects the soil around a previously driven pile, and therefore affects its capacity. So, there is some limit on the value of a load test of a single pile. Unfortunately, it is too expensive and impractical to attempt to load test a group of piles. The magnitude of loads required in the test is tremendous.

Class B Systems

Sliding Resistance

In addition to the previously described aspects for selecting the size of a footing, so as not to overstress the soil, there is another consideration which may affect the size of a footing. In certain columns, particularly in rigid frame buildings, there will exist a substantial horizontal force, usually directed outward and tending to cause *sliding*. This force can be resisted by use of one of the following methods:

- Tension Ties
- "Hairpin" Rods
- Shear Blocks

Tension Ties

A rod may be connected from a column (or pier) to the column (or pier) on the opposite side of the building, thus balancing the horizontal forces. (See Figure 8-12.) The size of the required tension rod may be easily determined as follows:

$$A_r = \frac{H}{F_t}$$

where:

A_r = Required Cross-sectional area of the rod. (sq. in.)

H = Horizontal Force (lbs.)

F_t = Allowable Stress in rod (p.s.i.)

= $0.6\,F_y$

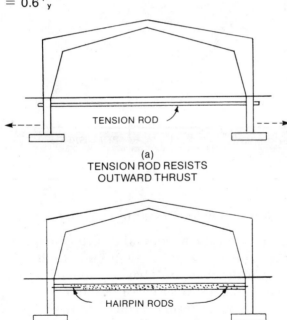

(a)
TENSION ROD RESISTS
OUTWARD THRUST

(b)
HAIRPIN RODS IN FLOOR SLAB
RESIST OUTWARD THRUST

Figure 8-12. Tension Rod Resists Horizontal Forces

Hairpin Rods

Another method of resisting horizontal forces involves use of a bent re-bar ("hairpin") which is cast into the slab-on-grade. The slab-on-grade, if properly reinforced, can provide the required resistance to the horizontal shear force. The force is transferred from the column to a tie rod or bent re-bar, to the concrete (through bond with the re-bar), and then into the mesh in the slab which acts as the final tensile element. Figure 8-13 illustrates the use of the spread tie for resisting horizontal thrusts. It is, of course, possible to use a combination of "across ties" and "spread ties" to resist the total horizontal thrusts.

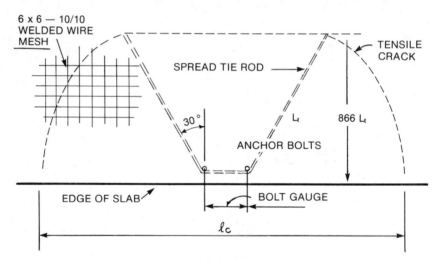

Figure 8-13. Spread Tie for Resisting Horizontal Thrusts

To adequately resist the horizontal thrusts, the spread tie rod must extend into the slab a sufficient distance so that the length of the "failure tensile crack" will have enough reinforcing mesh crossing it—such that a proper factor of safety is developed.

If the angle of the crack from the end of the ties is 45 degrees to the edge of the slab, and if the bolt gauge is assumed as zero (conservative), then the projected length of the tensile crack is:

$$\ell_c = 2(0.5)\,L_t + 2(.866L)\,L_t$$

$$= L_t + 1.732\,L_t = 2.732\,L_t$$

For 6 x 6 - 10/10 mesh, the steel cross-sectional area is 0.029 in square footage. Using an allowable stress of 20,000 psi for the mesh, the total tensile force resisting the opening of the "tensile crack" (including a factor of safety) is:

$$F_t = 0.029\ (20{,}000)\ (2.732)\ L_t = 1584\ L_t$$

Thus, if the horizontal force is 12,000 pounds, the required length (L_t) of the spread tie is 12,000 divided by 1584 = 7.57 feet. The following table gives the value of the tensile force across the crack for various sizes of mesh and re-bars.

Slab.Reinforcing or Mesh	Tensile Force as a Function of Tie length (lbs.) (L_t in Feet)
6 x 6 — 10/10	1584 L_t
6 x 6 — 8/8	2239 L_t
6 x6 — 6/6	3168 L_t
6 x 6 — 6/6 (2 layers)	6336 L_t
# 4 @ 12"	10,924 L_t
# 5 @ 12"	16,932 L_t
# 5 @ 8"	26,571 L_t

It is essential to note that the distance length must also be long enough to develop (in Bond) the strength of the re-bar used as the spread tie. The following table gives the development length for various sizes of re-bar spread ties.

Re-Bar Grade 40 or Better	Minimum L_t 3000 psi Concrete or Better
# 4	12"
# 5	14"
# 6	20"
# 7	27"
# 8	35"
# 9	44"

In order for the slab-on-grade to function effectively as a tension tie, it is essential that the slab not settle excessively, to the extent that the necessary tension cannot be developed. It is the opinion of the authors that if the slab-on-grade is to be used as the tension element, *no chances* can be taken on whether or not the slab "might" settle. It simply must not settle excessively. This means no soft compressible or organic soils may exist below the slab.

Shear Blocks

In certain structures, it may not be possible to provide these tension ties or hairpin rods. The only means by which the horizontal forces can be resisted, to prevent sliding, is by either friction between footing and soil, use of a shear block, or a combination of the two. (Retaining walls must commonly provide resistance to sliding, and use this method to do so.) A minimum factor of safety of 2.0* should exist against sliding. Friction between footing and soil is the easiest and most logical method of preventing sliding. The maximum friction force between footing and soil may be calculated from the following equation:

$$F_{max} = \mu N$$

where: F_{max} = Maximum Friction Force

N = Total Normal Force
(Column load plus weight of footing which exists under the same conditions causing the horizontal force to be resisted)

μ = coefficient of friction = 0.5
(0.5 is a conservative value for μ)

When the friction force is insufficient to resist the total horizontal force (with a proper factor of safety), it may be necessary to add a shear block. A shear block is nothing more than a depression on the bottom of a footing as shown in Figure 8-14.

The shear block *must* be placed in undisturbed virgin soil. The resistance to sliding from the shear block comes from development of what is technically referred to as "passive pressure." If the shear block cannot be constructed at the steep 1½:12 slope, it is then necessary to deepen the footing to provide the necessary

*For wind and/or earthquake the factor of safety reduces to 1.5.

passive pressure.*

Figure 8-15 illustrates the manner in which this passive pressure is developed by a shear block.

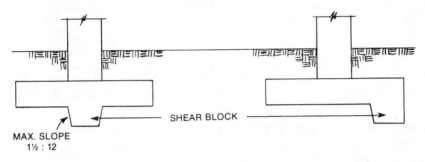

Figure 8-14.

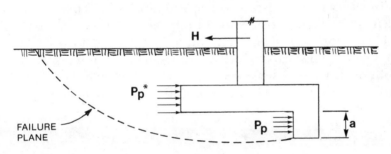

Figure 8-15.

With the horizontal force directed to the left, there is a tendency for the footing to slide in that direction. Passive pressure forces (Pp) resist this movement. In much the same mechanism as occurs in the bearing capacity failure, the footing with a shear block can slide *only* when the soil fails along the "failure plane" shown. The amount of resistance which the soil will develop, and the exact length and extent of the failure plane, will depend on the same soil properties, c, ø, and density which are found in the bearing capacity equations. Clearly, the total resistance which can be developed is also heavily dependent on the depth "a" of the shear block.

The sizing of the shear block is a relatively complex problem

---

*This passive pressure may be used only when the footing is poured into natural ground without forming.

involving a knowledge of earth pressure theory, and is beyond the scope of this book. What must be emphasized is that there are times when sliding cannot be resisted by friction alone, and a shear block must be used. An experienced soil engineer should be consulted for the design.

Piers and Grade Beams

There are two important elements in the building column-foundation system that should be included here, even though they are reinforced concrete elements, and not a part of the basic metal building system. Therefore, we include a discussion of pier and grade beam design, since these elements are often an intergral part of the foundation system.

Piers

In the general sense, a pier is a reinforced concrete "column element" which transfers load from the column to the footing. This "column element" must transfer the axial load, bending moments, and shears (which result from horizontal forces in the columns). In this sense, a pier is a highly complex element, subject to up to three loading conditions. Figure 8-16 illustrates the basic loading elements in pier design.

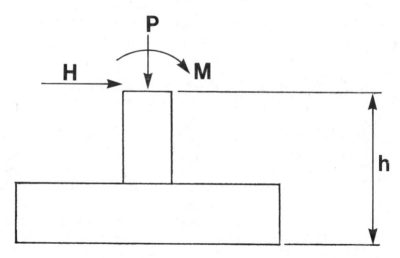

Figure 8-16.

In order to design a pier, it is necessary to fully understand the behavior of the reinforced concrete column. Structural engineers are well aware that a reinforced concrete column is one of the most complex structural elements that must be designed.

Since the pier is a reinforced concrete column subjected to axial load plus bending, it may be possible to utilize various handbooks to select pier size and reinforcement. The CRSI Handbook, for example, has tables wherein the size and reinforcement can be determined for a given axial load, plus moment. Using these tables would involve a "search" procedure, and there are many possible solutions to any one design problem. (Large pier—small reinforcement, small pier—large reinforcement.)

In general, the pier size will be dictated by the size of the column base plate, and provision of adequate "side" concrete cover on the anchor bolts and pier re-bars. Only in rare cases would the size of the pier need to be larger than the above, to satisfy structural requirements. Horizontal ties (usually #3 re-bars) would be used to hold the vertical pier reinforcement in place, to provide a horizontal tie to prevent buckling of the vertical re-bars under the column load, and to act as web reinforcement in the event that large shearing forces exist in a pier subject to horizontal loads.* It should be obvious how really important the ties are.

It is also important to emphasize the fact that the pier often becomes a *highly congested* reinforced concrete element. There could be, at a given cross-section, anchor bolts, pier re-bars, footing dowels, and horizontal ties. This area of concrete, as stated previously, can be highly stressed. Thus, it may be necessary to increase the size of a pier (larger than required structurally), simply to avoid congestion, and to enable the placement of concrete. Elevations of a "short" and "long" pier are shown in Figure 8-17.

The difference between a "short" and "long" pier would be the presence of *both* pier re-bars and footing dowels in the "long pier." Footing dowels may be used as pier reinforcement, until they become so long as to become unwieldy, when projecting out of the footing. There is no "magic dimension" which is an upper limit on dowel extension, but anything above six feet does, in the

---

*When ties are used as web reinforcement (stirrups) due to the existence of high shearing forces, the spacing of ties must be selected on the basis of separate design.

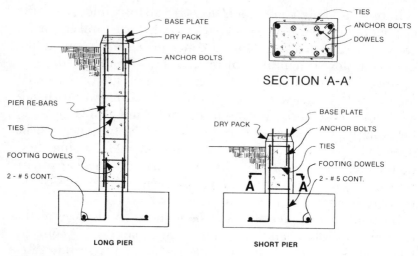

Figure 8-17.

opinion of the authors, become "too long." Sometimes the pier will be constructed as part of a wall or grade beam system as shown in Figure 8-18.

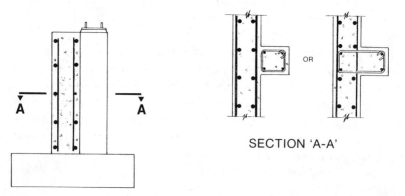

Figure 8-18. Pier and Grade Beam

Grade Beams

A grade beam is a reinforced concrete member spanning between column footings. It is constructed at or below "grade," and usually serves as support for the exterior wall construction of a building. A wall footing and short wall section could be used in place of a grade beam. Figure 8-19 illustrates a grade beam and wall section for comparison. A grade beam would normally be used when soils are poor, and all loads are carried on pile or caisson caps at column locations.

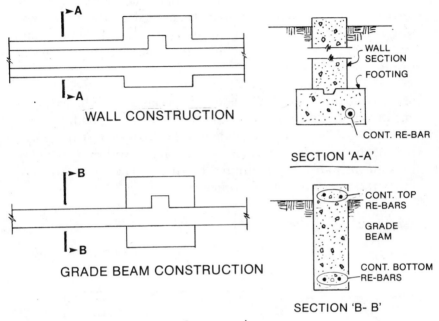

Figure 8-19. Grade Beam Construction

If the exterior wall of a structure is "heavy," such as in masonry construction, the load on the grade beam will be large, and a deep beam with considerable reinforcement may be required. A grade beam should be deep enough to extend below frost depth. Since the loads on a grade beam are *not* transmitted downward into the soil, the soil conditions under a grade beam are not of major concern. In the northern areas, where frost depth is commonly four feet or more, the grade beam depth is deep enough "automatically," such that minimal reinforcement will be needed to enable the grade beam to carry considerable loadings.

Since a grade beam is generally continuous over the tops of

footings, pile caps, or caissons, there will be some areas of tension on the top of the grade beam (near footings), and other areas of tension on the bottom (midway between footings). For this reason, it is common practice to reinforce grade beams with continuous re-bars, top and bottom, as shown in Figure 8-19.

For heavy exterior wall loads and a shallow grade beam, vertical web reinforcement may be needed to resist shearing forces. In general, a designer would try to make the grade beam deep enough (or wide enough) so that web reinforcement would not be required.

There is one special condition which occurs relative to grade beam construction, which deserves special attention here, primarily due to the wide usage and economy of the method. This relates to use of a shallow grade beam which is constructed as a part of the floor slab construction, as shown in Figure 8-20 (a). In some instances, a column "footing" may be constructed in a similar manner as illustrated in Figure 8-20 (b).

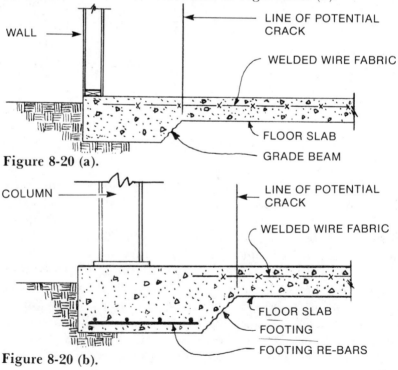

Figure 8-20 (a).

Figure 8-20 (b).

The use of a shallow "grade beam," poured as a part of the floor slab, is common, particularly in warmer climates where frost depth is minimum. In such cases, the major consideration is to have the "grade beam" founded below organic materials (top soil), below disturbed ground (cultivated, planted, tree root zones), and below any depths to which erosion from rainfall, roof, or downspout runoff might extend. A crack will almost surely occur in the floor slab at the point where the "grade beam" starts. (See Figures 8-20 (a) and (b).)

The use of a shallow "footing" poured as a part of the floor slab (thickened slab) is a complex condition. The authors are aware that this particular footing is in common use. There are some limitations to the use of such a system. Consider, for example, the footing shown in Figure 8-21. Assume the footing is subject to a reversible moment and a vertical, downward column load.

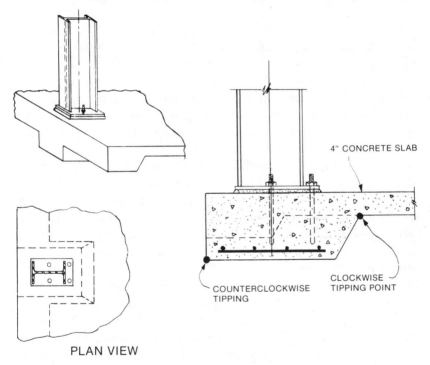

PLAN VIEW

Figure 8-21. Thickened Slab Footing

The entire stability (overturning) and soil pressure analysis is predicated on the fact that *only the footing* is available to resist the overturning moment. As a result, a substantial mass of concrete is needed to provide a proper factor of safety.

In the case of the "thickened slab" however, an entirely different condition exists. If, in Figure 8-21, the column moment is clockwise, the following is the case. In order for the "footing" to tip about the "clockwise tipping point," the footing (3' 0" x 3' 0" section), and some portion of the grade beam, must also tip. The grade beam would be poured monolithically with the footing, and it is impossible for the footing to tip without raising the grade beam. In addition to raising some length of grade beam, a portion of the slab would also have to be either "picked up" or "sheared off" of the rest of the slab. The slab and grade beam weights provide a considerable stabilizing force against a clockwise moment.

For the counterclockwise moment, a different mechanism exists. Here the grade beam is located near the "counterclockwise tipping point," and is of little value in resisting overturning. However, before the "footing" can tip, it must literally tear out of the slab. The shearing strength of the concrete slab (even as thin as 4"), provides a considerable force which resists "tearing out," and thus stabilizes the footing. The concrete slab will provide resistence to "tearing out," provided that reinforcement actually crosses the line of a potential crack. In the case of the thickened slab, there is every possibility that under actual field conditions, the slab mesh will be "on the ground," and be ineffective in tying the "footing" to the balance of the slab. For this reason, the authors do not recommend counting on the slab shearing resistance for stability. As a result, the thickened slab should be used only when moments are small. The exact value of an acceptable moment must be evaluated for the specific project.

A major disadvantage of this system occurs when geographical location required a deep, thick footing to get below frost. In such cases, it will generally be cheaper to pour an individual footing. If a "thickened slab" footing can be used, the size, reinforcement, and construction jointing should be selected by someone experienced with concrete design.

Finally, there is one other practical aspect of the thickened slab footing which should be noted. This applies to those regions of the country where expansive soils are commonly encountered. It should be obvious that expansive soils acting on a shallow footing could cause tremendous damage to the floor and/or roof systems. This shallow, thickened slab is not recommended where expansive soils exist, even when other previously noted conditions are satisfied.

Foundation Construction

This section includes two basic areas which will be covered. The first relates to overall construction of foundations, as dictated by engineering requirements. This will include proper preparation of soil, placing of reinforcing, forming, etc. The second area relates to installation of anchor bolts. This has been a particularly important field problem, and requires special attention.

General Construction Requirements

The first and most significant point that should be made relates to comments, made here several times, about the variability of soils. Footing depths are established all too often from a limited number of soil borings. It is entirely possible that the proposed elevation for a given footing is inappropriate, due to a localized pocket of weak, soft, compressible, or organic materials. The authors firmly believe that the decision regarding the adequacy (or inadequacy) of the soil bearing at a particular footing location should be that of the design engineer. The excavator, forms carpenter, or concrete contractor should not be permitted to decide on the proper base elevation for a footing, and especially should not be permitted to raise (or lower) footings from the elevation shown on the drawings, without written approval.

On the other hand, the designer should encourage and request contractors to alert him to any questionable soil conditions. A concerned, observant contractor is a welcome addition to the total construction "team."

If the foundations are to be placed on clay soils, use can effectively be made of the pocket penetrometer. This instrument is especially valuable in locating the poor, soft soils which are improper for use in the structure. Low readings may suggest deepening the footings to get below the "soft spot."

Portland cement concrete will set up under water. This means that footings can be placed, even if the excavation is full of water. However, the water-cement ratio would go up considerably under such conditions, and the mix design would have to be adjusted to account for the extra water. It is preferred procedure to pump any water from the excavation, prior to placing concrete.

The bottom of footing excavations should be flat and level, free from debris and large rocks and organic materials. Reinforcing bars should be spaced uniformly, per the plans, on bricks or other *stable* support. Bars which fall from their supports during placing operations are likely to be structurally ineffective.

The authors have had numerous experiences with the question of whether it is necessary to form footings, or whether the concrete may be "poured in the hole" without form work. It is our opinion that form work is not necessary, and adds an unneeded expense to the job. There may in fact be a structural benefit to not using forms. This comes from the fact that when forms are used, the space between the form and the side of the hole must be filled. This space may be narrow, and it will be difficult to compact the soil placed in this area. Without forms, the concrete fills all the spaces, and no compaction is needed. Clearly, for footings in loose sands or sandy silts, formwork will be required. Many local building codes *require* that footings be formed.

A danger which may result from not using forms relates to having the footing end up being *too thin*. One can only caution the need for inspection of all footing construction. Once the footings are back filled, there is little that can be done, short of expensive underpinning, in the event of a "mistake."

An important aspect of footing construction relates to concrete placement. Often, the footing will be considerably below the ground surface, and the tendency will be to "drop" the concrete into the hole rather than place it. Concrete should not be *dropped* into forms. Dropping causes segregation and resulting poor quality. Concrete *dropped* through a deep pier is especially poor. The paste will stick to the bars and forms, while the coarse aggregate drops to the bottom. This condition is common, and results in exceptionally poor concrete quality.

Use of vibration is helpful to avoid segregation. Vibrators are commonly used to improve the overall uniformity of concrete in all types of construction. It is especially useful in cases where concrete placement is difficult. (Most people in the construction business use the expression "pouring concrete." Strictly speaking, concrete should be placed; concrete should not be wet enough to be "poured.") Both experience and research have shown that vibration cannot be overdone in concrete. Vibration is an effective means of insuring that the concrete will be adequately bonded to reinforcing bars and anchor bolts.

Reinforcing bars should be placed to the accuracy required by the ACI Code. This generally means a $\pm \frac{1}{4}''$ placement tolerance.

Anchor Bolts

Anchor bolts play a multiple role in the footing-column interaction.

1) Anchor bolts serve to connect column to footing (or pier) *in the right location.* Properly located and positioned anchor bolts will almost assure proper fit of structural members previously mentioned. Since anchor bolts are so critical to proper alignment of the column, they are always located with a template. The common steel used for anchor bolts is ASTM A307.

2) Anchor bolts hold columns during erection of the structure. In many buildings, it is common and accepted practice to use the anchor bolts to support columns until beams and X-bracing can be installed. The authors are aware of a recent situation in which 12" long anchor bolts were to be installed in a spread footing. The footing was to be 16 inches thick, but was constructed only 10 inches thick. The anchor bolts were pushed or "stuck" into the wet concrete, and in leaving the proper projection of the bolt out of the top of the concrete, the workman pushed the hook through the footing and down into the soil. Obviously, the anchor bolt hook was totally ineffective (being anchored in the soil). An iron worker was *severely* injured when the column and beam on which he was working (30 feet in the air) tipped over. The anchor bolts simply pulled out of the concrete, until

the hook caught on the bottom of the footing. This tragic story has a number of significant messages for all of us.

3) Anchor bolts transfer vertical uplift forces from column to footing.

4) Anchor bolts transfer horizontal shearing forces from column to footing.

The most complex situation involving anchor bolts is the condition where large shears, in combination with high tensions or compressions, exist. Little reserch has been done on the strength of bolts anchored in concrete, and subject to combined stress effects. The pure shearing strength of the bolt itself is well known, but when the bolt is anchored in a concrete pier or footing, it is the concrete that controls the bolt capacity.

There are a number of factors that are significant in terms of the use of anchor bolts:

a) Proper confinement of the concrete between and around these bolts is essential. The most effective means yet developed is the use of horizontal bent re-bars or ties around the bolts to form a "bolt cage."

b) A proper space must be maintained between anchor bolts and ties, so that concrete can be properly placed. The area in and around the anchor bolts is likely to be highly congested, and concrete placement will be difficult at best. The authors are aware of a failure of one structure, requiring major, expensive repairs, because the pier into which the anchor bolt cage was placed was so congested that concrete could not be properly placed around the bolts and ties. As soon as the column horizontal shear force (due to the roof dead load) was developed, the piers exhibited major spalling and cracking, and the ensuing examination revealed major voids in the concrete.

c) Properly positioned, tightened anchor bolts are the only means by which a column moment may be transferred to a footing or pier. If this assumption is made in the design, and the footing is designed for this moment, then the proper moment transfer is both reasonable and warranted.

Anchor bolts generally develop their anchorage capability from two sources. First, there is a basic adhesion of the concrete to the anchor bolt. This "adhesive bond" accounts for a portion of the anchorage strength. The other aspect of anchorage is called "mechanical bond." This comes from the mechanical anchorage of the head of the bolt, if a standard bolt is used, or from the bent leg of the bolt which is hooked into the concrete.

Slabs-on-Grade

This final section will deal with the design (selection of thickness and reinforcement) of slabs-on-grade, subject to uniform, partial uniform, and concentrated vertical loads. The first and most important point that can be made is that, if a slab-on-grade is resting on a uniform, high quality soil, and is loaded with a *perfectly uniform load*, the slab thickness can be, essentially, minimum, and, theoretically, no reinforcement would be needed. The reason this is true is that reinforcement is required to resist *bending*, and a uniformly-supported, uniformly-loaded slab will not bend; hence, no flexural steel is required. Therefore, statements such as "design a slab-on-grade for 2500 pounds per square foot" are (by themselves) meaningless.

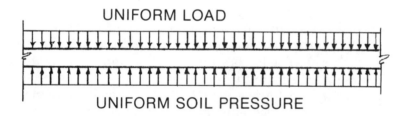

NOTE: The slab will not bend under this loading.

Figure 8-22. Uniformly Loaded Slab-on-Grade

However, engineers have learned from experience that a floor in a factory, which will have heavy storage loadings (perhaps steel storage, heavy castings, etc.) *averaging* 2500 psf, will undoubtedly have localized concentrations of load and aisles. The simplest example of this is the use of dunnage or blocking to support equipment, materials, storage racks, or wheel loads as shown in Figure 8-23. The exaggerated slab curvature is shown. This curvature (bending) will result in stresses in the slab for which reinforcement may be required. Therefore, a heavy industrial floor loading will really *not* be uniformly loaded, but rather will have load concentrations, as shown in the figure. The designer must carefully examine the design of a slab-on-grade to determine whether or not concentrated loads and resulting bending will exist.

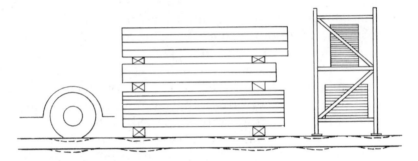

Figure 8-23. Typical Loads to a Slab-on-Grade

There are other reasons for reinforcing to be placed in a slab-on-grade. Principal among these are temperature and shrinkage effects. The ACI Code does not strictly require reinforcing in slabs-on-grade. A committee of ACI for Design of Slabs-on-Grade was only recently formed in 1975. Clearly, there are many instances of lightly loaded slabs on good soils, wherein reinforcing may not be required. In such cases, the designer should expect random cracks due to shrinkage and temperature. The authors do not recommend construction of slabs-on-grade without reinforcing. Welded wire mesh is normally used for the slab reinforcement.

Slabs-on-grade will be affected by concrete shrinkage and temperature. The concrete will want to change dimensionally, and will be restrained from such change by the soil. The presence of reinforcing (mesh) *will not prevent cracking* of the the slab, but will cause a distribution of hairline cracks which will generally not be noticeable.

Designers have learned, however, that the presence of reinforcement will not guarantee a floor without observable cracks, and that use of crack control joints is generally logical. The use of crack control joints is based on the logic that it is better (from an appearance point of view) to have a crack occur in a prepared straight line joint, rather than to exist in a random, non-linear manner. The reader should note that the *crack will be there,* in either case, and that the joint simply defines its location and appearance.

Generally, crack control joints should be constructed at locations of potential cracks. There are countless examples which exist in structures where a random crack occurs only a few inches away from an "uncracked crack control joint." While this extension of Murphy's Law (whatever can go wrong—will go wrong) does occur, the authors do believe that proper and extensive use of crack control joints is in keeping with good engineering practice. The general intent is to place crack control joints in the location where cracks are likely to occur. Figure 8-24 shows typical locations for crack control joints, in the vicinity of columns where cracks have traditionally formed. In general, the attempt is to minimize the size of pours to areas which are 15 to 25 feet in length. Figure 8-25 gives typical details of crack control joints.

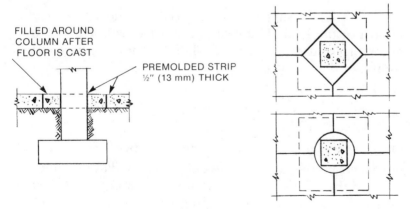

Figure 8-24. Crack Control Joint Locations

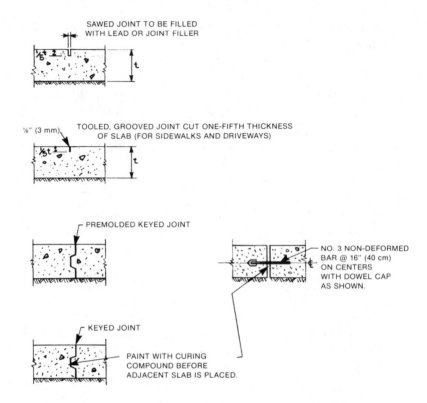

Figure 8-25. Crack Control and Construction Joints

A slab-on-grade subjected to a concentrated load will bend in the area of the load. This bending must be resisted by proper reinforcing, and/or an adequate slab thickness. The amount of bending of the slab depends upon a number of factors:

1) The magnitude of the load.

2) The modulus of elasticity of the slab concrete. Use Ec = 3,000,000 psi for this manual.

3) The moment of inertia of the slab (depends on thickness).

4) The compressibility of the soil is measured by the subgrade modulus. This property is not commonly measured in routine soil boring and testing procedures. It may be approximated roughly from "blow count" taken in the stan-

dard penetration tests for granular soils, and from the unconfined compression strength for cohesive soils.

5) Size of the loaded area.

6) Poissons ratio for concrete ($u = 0.15$). This is a constant property of concrete which relates the deformations which occur in one direction, as a result of stresses applied in a perpendicular direction.

The equations used to design a slab-on-grade are based on a theory developed by Westergaard, and are quite complex. This book was not intended to develop that level of complex structural theory. Most engineers would resort to the "rule of thumb" approach given in Table 8-26 for design of slabs-on-grade. A very large, permanent, concentrated load should have a separate footing.

Use	Floor Loading	Slab Thickness	Reinforcing*
Commercial	100-200 psf	5"	6 x 6 - 10/10
Industrial	400-500 psf	6"	6 x 6 - 6/6
Industrial	600-800 psf	6"	6 x 6 - 7/6 (2 layers)
Industrial	1500 psf	7"	# 4 @ 12" E.W. (2 layers)
Industrial	2500 psf	8"	# 5 @ 12" E.W. (2 layers)
Industrial	3500 psf	9"	# 5 @ 8" E.W. (2 layers)

Designations for mesh have officially changed. This book uses the convention most familiar to engineers and contractors.

Table 8-26. Slab-on-Grade Design Table

A common problem, often encountered by the authors, in conjunction with slab-on-grade design, relates to placing such slabs on low-quality, compressible and/or variable-thickness soils. In general, the compressibility of the soil is not a major consideration, as far as the design of the slab is concerned. The subgrade modulus would be affected, but the worst that might happen is that a thicker, or more heavily reinforced, slab might be required.

The problem is that such slabs-on-grade will settle; and may settle non-uniformly. Increasing the slab thickness, or adding reinforcement, will not solve this problem. All too often, designers become so concerned with the building foundations, that the consideration of slab-on-grade settlements is overlooked.

There is no magic solution to this problem. If the compressible soils are shallow, they may be removed, and replaced with a compacted, engineered backfill. If the problem soils are of a considerable depth, then it may be necessary to replace the slab-on-grade with a structural slab. A structural slab could be supported by a number of different methods, including caissons, piles, grade beams, and foundation walls.

The earth may be used as a "form," but the assumption is that it may not be counted upon to support floor loads, and will eventually settle, leaving a gap under the slab. The structural slab will be considerably thicker and more heavily reinforced, than the slabs-on-grade presented previously.

9
Codes and Design Specifications

Design Specifications

Design, fabrication, and erection of metal building systems and all other structures are governed by various standard specifications. The actual design of a structure is specified in the ACI, AISI, and AISC specifications. ACI specifies the design of concrete, which is not directly used in designing metal building systems, but is required for foundation design. The design of the metal building system is governed by the AISI and AISC specifications. The AISI specification is used to design all cold-formed members in a metal building system, such as wall panel, roof deck, purlins, and girts. The design of the structural frame is governed by AISC.

These design specifications establish criteria that enable the engineer to check the strength and stability of the members in a building. Typically, the specifications will establish safe, allowable stress levels that cannot be exceeded upon application of design loads. The engineer is responsible for analyzing a structure and calculating the stresses in the various structural members. In order for the design to be acceptable, the allowable stresses must not be exceeded. This will insure that a structure has adequate strength to carry the design loads.

It is possible to design a member with adequate strength to support a given load, but with inadequate stiffness. Excessive deflection may result, even though allowable stresses are not exceeded. These deflections can cause damage to non-structural elements, such as partitions and ceilings, or the deflections can just be visually displeasing.

It is essential to point out that these design specifications are almost universally accepted in the USA as *the* way in which structures are to be designed. They are included by reference in most building codes. Therefore, to meet governing building code requirements, as discussed in the next section, designs must follow provisions outlined in AISI, AISC, and ACI.

Building Codes and Zoning Regulations

Building codes are legal documents (enacted by law) which give *miminum* requirements with which buildings must comply in order to be granted a building permit in a particular city or state. These codes govern such topics as:

- Height and area restrictions
- Room size requirements
- Required methods of design (e.g. ACI, AISC, AISI, etc.)
- Miminum design loads (e.g. wind, snow)
- Building materials
- Plumbing requirements
- Handicap requirements
- Heating, ventilating, and air-conditioning
- Mechanical equipment
- Sprinkler requirements

Designers are particularly interested in design load requirements defined in these codes. Wind, snow, and earthquake loading greatly affect the size of members that comprise a metal

building system. Sprinkler, mechanical, and plumbing requirements can also affect member sizes, since these different utilities
may be supported by the building structure. Exit and entrance
requirements must be reviewed, so that the manufacturer will
know the location and quantity of doors to be provided.

The owner, as well as the metal building contractor, must be
aware of the building code(s) having jurisdiction in the location
of the planned building. It may be a city, county, state, or model
building code. The local building official will be able to advise
the owner and contractor as to the appropriate code to follow.

There are four major, independently developed, model building codes in the country. These may be adopted wholly or in part
by a state or city. They are:

1) The Standard Building Code — By the Southern Building
   Code Congress, Inc.

2) The Uniform Building Code — By the International Conference of Building Officials.

3) The Basic Building Code — By the Building Officials and
   Code Administration.

4) The National Building Code — By the American Insurance Association.

The first three are "consensus" codes. That is, they are promulgated and revised by building officials, industry representatives,
or any other interested parties. Anyone desiring to make a change
to one of these codes can propose it in writing, and be assured that
his proposal will have a public hearing before a review committee,
and will, after one year, be put to a vote of the membership. The
fourth code mentioned is developed by the insurance industry,
and has no such consensus policy.

Another set of regulations that any building system must
satisfy is the zoning laws. Zoning laws are established by municipalities in order to control the growth and development of
communities. These laws (restrictions) are established by local
officials, are subject to change at any time, and establish or
earmark certain areas as being zoned for residential, commercial,
or industrial development. An owner must be aware of the zoning
laws governing his property, because these laws will define the

type of building he can construct on the land, and the type of activity that can take place in the building. Zoning laws may also restrict such things as building height, building size, property size, and appearance. Typically, an owner desiring to construct a new building will have to submit architectural elevations of his proposed building to a zoning committee, or building review board, for their approval.

Before a new building can be constructed, the owner must satisfy all of the required codes and regulations previously mentioned. The first step usually is satisfying local zoning ordinances, and getting approval by the zoning committee. The next step is designing the building to satisfy the governing building code. Both engineering calculations and building drawings must usually be submitted to the governing body for approval. Most states require both the calculations and drawings to be stamped with the seal of a registered professional engineer or architect. These stamped calculations and drawings will then be reviewed for compliance with the building codes and design specifications. After all code regulations have been met, the owner will receive a building permit which enables him to begin construction on his site. Some states will also require that periodic inspections of construction be performed by a registered professional engineer or architect. State or local building inspectors may also periodically visit the construction site. The purpose of these inspections is to insure that the building is being constructed according to the approved plans, using accepted construction techniques.

Fire Codes

Most building codes have specifications dealing with fire protection. Fire protection has a significant effect on metal building systems, since the structural frame of most systems is exposed to this hazard. Building codes specify an hourly rating based on building usage and occupancy. The hourly rating establishes the minimum amount of time that a particular structural element must be capable of performing without "failure" during a fire.* During a fire, steel will begin to lose its strength as its temperature increases (see Figure 9-1), and must therefore be protected in order to prevent the weakening process from occurring.

*See Chapter 13 for a more detailed explanation of fire testing and fire rating requirements.

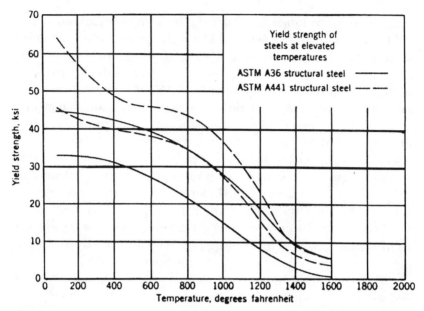

Figure 9-1.

The protection usually consists of a sprayed-on coating or encasement using fire resistive materials. The thickness of the protective coating is determined by the hourly fire rating required.

Assembly occupancies such as churches, schools, theaters, and institutions may require fire ratings of up to four hours. Buildings in which highly combustible materials are stored or used also may require high ratings. Warehouses, in which non-combustible material is stored, usually require only a low fire rating, and in some cases, no rating is required. In addition to establishing fire ratings on various structural members, the building codes also establish requirements for fire separation, automatic fire suppression systems, occupancy separation, height and area limits, and property line set backs, to name a few.

Testing Procedures

The American Society for Testing Materials (ASTM) has established material specifications and testing methods which are used extensively by metal building systems manufacturers. Material used in the fabrication of metal building systems must meet ASTM specifications. An ASTM specification for a particular steel will include chemical composition, mechanical properties, and methods for testing the steel to verify its performance. The manufacturer will normally refer to an ASTM specification when ordering the building materials. The standardization that results from usage of the ASTM specifications prevents confusion when dealing with different suppliers, and insures a uniform product. ASTM also specifies standard tests to be used to determine composition, fire resistance, and physical properties of various materials. Independent testing laboratories, such as Underwriters Laboratories, use these standard tests to accomplish their work.

The structural frame of a metal building system is typically a welded plate girder. The welding processes and details used were developed by the American Welding Society (AWS). AWS has tested the strength and performance of many different types of welded joints. The most commonly used joints, which have exhibited high quality and performance, have been standardized, and are known as pre-qualified joints. Welded joints, which do not fall into this category, must be structurally tested under anticipated loads before using. AWS specifies this testing procedure as well as weld material, welding processes, pre-heating requirements, and surface preparation.

10
Legal and Contractual Considerations

The purpose of this chapter is to provide the reader with a concise summary of pertinent aspects of the contractual considerations associated with the metal building industry. By contractual considerations are meant that broad area of topics including:

Contract Law Concepts

Agency Concepts

Contract Documents

Warranties and Guarantees

Lien Concepts

Professional Liability

Bonds

Certainly, this chapter cannot replace advice from competent legal counsel. To expect this is unrealistic, and in fact, dangerous. What this chapter can do is acquaint the reader with general concepts and guidelines to enable him or her to interact more intelligently with one's clients and attorney.

Contract Law Concepts

Contract law exists to protect *reasonable* expectations of the parties to the contract. Much of what is done in the business world is done on the basis of expecting promises to be kept. The law permits (with some limited exceptions) parties to determine *for themselves* what their respective obligations are, under the terms of a contract, provided the two parties are of reasonably equal bargaining power (which is usually the case in building contracts). If the bargaining power of the parties is not equal, a court may decide that a particular contract provision is "unconscionable," as it could and would not have resulted from arm's-length negotiations. In such a situation, the court will declare the provision void and unenforceable—as frequently occurs with respect to disclaimers.

Contracts can be classified in different ways. One way is to classify them by the method of their creation. "Implied contracts" are contracts manifested by acts rather than words (i.e., getting in a cab and asking to be taken somewhere *implies* that you will pay). In the world of construction, the "express" (written) contract is the common contract type. Contracts can be classified as to being "negotiated" or "adhered to." An example of an "adhered to" contract is the purchase of a car. This contract is a pre-printed form in which blanks are "filled in," and for which only the purchaser's signature is required. The common type of contract in the building industry is the negotiated contract, where both parties have input, and actual negotiation of terms is involved.

Agency Concepts

Contracts in this country (in general) must show a "meeting of the minds" to be enforced. The parties named in the contract, the "principals," often are artificial entities, such as corporations, trusts, and partnerships, which, obviously, cannot themselves negotiate and execute contracts. This is done by an "agent"—an individual, firm, or corporation which the "principal" has legally authorized to act for it. The concept of agency is complex, but in general, the following persons are clearly agents of their organizations:

- The owner of a sole proprietorship
- A general partner in a partnership
- The chief executive officer of a corporation
- A purchasing agent of a corporation

An office manager, who routinely buys office supplies in the
$200-$500 cost range, probably is not an agent, if he entered into a
contract to purchase a $50,000 computer system on behalf of
his company. A subsidiary normally is not an agent of its parent
corporation, nor authorized to create contractual obligations for
it. And, similarly, a corporation is not an agent of its individual
shareholders. Frequently, principals are represented by "advi-
sors," such as lawyers, whose authority to act usually is quite
limited, as well as by "agents." And, of course, principals can
authorize agents to act for them in particular aspects of a project.
For example, owners frequently appoint architects to act as their
agents in reviewing plans and specifications, and in overseeing
erection work.

Finally, there must be a "consideration" to support the contract. No legal system enforces all promises—some are contrary to
public policy, and others are not important enough to enforce
(promises to take a child to the zoo, and compaign promises of
elected officials are not enforceable—although in the latter case,
we might consider changing the law)! A promise must be
accompanied by benefits to one party and detriments to the other.
The law does *not* look for monetary "fairness." "Consideration"
involves exchanges of promises, and the law looks for a meeting
of the minds, or a "bargain." The consideration can be "present"
or "future" in terms of time. Present consideration consists of
promises exchanged for promises or acts. Future consideration—
"if you do this, I will (in the future) give you that"—is enforceable, if the person relied upon the promise, and acted in some
way.

Contract Documents

Two types of contract documents will be discussed in this
section:

1) Contractor/Owner Contract.

2) Contractor/Manufacturer Contract.

The contractor/owner contract is one that re-occurs and
changes with every project. Clearly, it is this contract that affects
the day-to-day operations, and probably the profit or loss picture

for a given organization. For that reason, major emphasis will be given to that contract.

The second contract, between contractor and manufacturer, is usually an event which does not re-occur. It happens at the outset of the relationship between the parties. As a result, this section is included to acquaint the reader with the general nature of such contracts (i.e., what generally is included), without major emphasis on contract formulation or other considerations.

Contractor/Owner Contract

The preparation of contracts—notwithstanding advice and consultation with legal counsel—does involve certain basic principles, which have been time-tested, and are therefore worth learning. Ideally, a contract should be written in language that readily can be understood by the parties and should not contain provisions of dubious enforceability, thus inviting litigation. In this regard, it is important to note that contract formation principles vary from state to state, so that it is essential to be aware of *applicable* law. A contract which is valid and enforceable in the state where its use was intended may be invalid and unenforceable, in whole or in part, in an adjoining state. Of particular interest, in this regard, are such areas as registration and licensing of contractors, and tax considerations. Non-compliance with applicable statutes can result in:

- Forfeiture of license
- Forfeiture of right to sue for goods or services supplied
- Prevention from obtaining future work

Another general principle, that is critical in the development of a "good" contract, is to prepare for all situations *in the contract.* This includes such topics as:

- Define what is included in the contract documents (addenda, change orders, etc.)
- Define the responsibilities of the parties to the contract
- Define contract sum
- Define how sub-contracts are handled
- Define how separate (but related) contracts are to be handled

- Determine which state law shall govern the contract
- Make sure that the parties' successors, partners, etc. are bound to the contract
- Determine precisely how notice shall be given regarding contract changes (registered mail, etc.)
- Determine how to handle royalties and patents
- Define how testing procedures will be handled (who pays)
- Define how disputes are to be settled (arbitration)
- Define time considerations (completion date, liquidated damages)
- Define how and when payments are to be made
- Define interest considerations when payments are not made
- Define responsibilities relative to safety
- Define insurance requirements
- Determine how to accommodate changes, including cost escalations
- Determine how to deal with correction of defective work
- Determine how the contract may be terminated

The contract between an owner and contractor would normally include the following documents:

The Agreement — This document is normally a brief statement in which the contract price and scope of project are defined.

The General Conditions — These conditions define the responsibilities of the parties to the contract.

The Drawings.

The Technical Specifications — These documents define the *quality* of products and materials which cannot be conveyed in the drawings.

The Supplementary Conditions — These delineate modifications to the general conditions to fit the specific needs of an individual project. Such concepts as insurance and bonding requirements are included.

In defining the responsibilities of the parties to the contract, it is essential that the parties do exactly what was agreed, *and no more*. If one party does extra work, or provides extra service, without the prior written approval of the other party (i.e., "volunteers"), that party also picks up added (unwanted) responsibility and may not be entitled to be paid for that work or service.

There are some authorities on contracts who believe that provisions regarding "liquidated damages" (an agreed sum of money to be paid in the event of a breach of contract) should be included in the basic document. The authors do not share this view. Provisions dealing with . . .

- Who pays damages?, and . . .
- What are the *real* damages? . . .

are always *the* principal contested items in any dispute. To expect parties to be able to agree *in advance* as to what reasonable damages are, in the event the contract is breached in some way, is not realistic. If the contract includes precise definitions of the responsibilities of the parties, the authors believe that is the best that can probably be attained.

Types of Construction Contracts

In the construction field, there are various types of contracts classified by how the price is established. The "lump sum" contract is the type commonly associated with competitively bid projects. Such a contract is reasonable, if costs are reasonably well known, and major cost escalation is not likely in the construction period. If costs are increasing rapidly, enough "fat" must be built into the price to protect the builder or contractor.

Since the "lump sum" contract is so commonly associated with "bidding," it is appropriate to include some pertinent comments about bidding at this time. From a contractual viewpoint, it is essential to realize that the bidding process is accompanied by published *rules*. Any deviation in the form of a bid from that prescribed in the rules could result in voiding the bid. This is always true in government projects. Thus, time and form requirements must be strictly adhered to. The builder should never assume anything. Bidding rules change, and the instructions to bidders should be studied and followed.

An alternative to the lump sum contract, which is more protective of the interest of the builder or contractor, is the "cost plus" contract, wherein the builder or contractor is paid exact costs (which are fully disclosed to the owner), *plus a fixed fee,* agreed upon in advance. This contract may be less desirable from the point of view of the owner, since the exact amount of the total cost is unknown until project completion.

Still another possible contractual arrangement is the "Design-Build" contract. There are many variations to this concept, but, for a fixed fee, the owner receives the entire project including design. The design can be provided by design professionals retained by the builder, or in some cases, by designers on the staff of the builder's organization. Such design-build projects are often referred to as "turnkey" projects, where the contract is signed, and the builder has the responsibility to totally complete the project, and "turn the key" over to the owner.

An important aspect of the design-build concept relates to what happens if the project does not proceed to completion—which, in times of high interest rates and rapid price inflation, is all too common. The contract agreement should clearly state the payment required for the design services, if the project is not built, and who owns the plans under these conditions. There are many examples of cases wherein contractors have not been paid for design services, because the contract did not spell out these requirements. Also, if a project does not go ahead, and the contractor is paid for design services, does the owner now own the plans? The contract language should be clear on this point. Many designers take the view that their design is copyrighted, and may not be used by others. Others believe that if they are paid, the plans belong to the owner, who may then use them as he sees fit.

Model Construction Contracts

Based on the preceding discussion of pertinent aspects of the contract documents, it should be clear that developing a fair and comprehensive contract is a complex challenge. For this reason alone, the authors strongly recommend the used of "form contracts"—for example, those published by the American Institute of Architects (AIA), Associated General Contractors (AGC), and the Metal Building Dealers Association (MBDA). The concept of a "fair" contract is important. Unfair ("unconscionable") contractual provisions are, at best, difficult to enforce. Also, the courts will generally *not* favor the party who draws up the contract in the event that the wording is ambiguous.

There are those who believe that standard contracts are only a guide, and that substantial modification is required to "customize" the contract. The authors do not share this view. Several years prior to this writing, the AIA documents, for example, had some serious shortcomings, particularly in the Owner/Architect Agreement. These have been largely eliminated. As a part of a standard form package, the "Supplementary Conditions" are a basic element. It is in this portion of the contract that modifications and/or additions to the pre-printed form copy should be made. Thus, with judicious use of the supplementary conditions, a contract *can be* customized to any extent that the parties desire.

It should be pointed out that the AIA form contract is occasionally criticized by established contractor/builders, in that portions of the wording tend to somewhat discriminate against the contractor/builder in favor of the owner and/or architect. The Metal Building Dealers Association has published a new form contract that will attempt to eliminate these inequities.

The MBDA form contract was thoroughly researched, and represents input from a variety of experienced metal building system contractors. It was also reviewed by several different attorneys (from various states) prior to publication. This very practical document is available through MBDA's national headquarters.

There is one special aspect of the contract formation process that should be emphasized. There is a tendency today on the part of the contractor to submit a proposal to a prospective client. Such proposals are usually brief, and include only basic concepts about what is to be contracted. Often, the proposal ends up *being* the contract. This is definitely not recommended. The proposal, normally, does not include all of the language required to protect the parties. To avoid problems with such a practice, the proposal should state that the general conditions and Standard Form of Agreement will form the *basis* of the contract, and that the proposal is intended to convey only broad information as to the scope and cost of the proposed project. In this way the proposal can never be the contract by itself. It is good practice to submit a blank copy of the Agreement, General Conditions, and Supplementary Conditions forms with the proposal.

All of the preceding material on contract documents relates to a written contract. Oral modifications to a contract will not be acceptable to most courts, particularly if this would result in a major change to the written concept. It is, at best, extremely difficult to prove that both parties agreed to a specific modification which is contrary to the interests of one and, therefore, will be denied by that party. If, however, the written contract is vague, or implies that certain items are to be agreed upon (a poor contract-writing practice), then an oral agreement can be enforceable. The best advice is to "get it in writing." If the written contract specifically excludes oral agreements, and requires changes to be in writing, then oral agreements are null and void.

Practical Guidelines

Since this book was developed for the benefit of the entire metal building systems industry, it is reasonable to include some practical guidelines for contract formulation which are "contractor oriented." These have been learned "the hard way" in many cases, and are submitted to prevent problems for both parties to the contract.

1) An investigation should be made of the other party. This means not only credit checks and Dun and Bradstreet evaluations, but general knowledge about specific contract performance in the past. (The contractor should expect the same study to be made about his organization.) As implied earlier in the discussion of agency concepts, credit checks and evaluations should not rely on the status of related corporations or of individual shareholders unless those third parties are going to guarantee performance of the contract.

2) Simply because a prospective contract is big, doesn't mean it is necessarily profitable.

3) If the project is in a state in which the contractor has not previously done work, it is essential to evaluate pertinent laws affecting construction contracts. The rights of both parties can be considerably different than anticipated.

4) The contract should provide for "front money." The psychology of contracting and reaching an agreement changes dramatically when the owner has paid and cannot get its funds back without litigation.

5) The contractor should endeavor to reduce or eliminate retainage whenever possible. Since contractors frequently work with net profits of less than 10%, a retainage (as little as 10%) can have an adverse affect on a contractor's cash flow, and seriously hamper his ability to properly, financially service the project. We must admit that some owners will be adamant on this subject, and retainage will be forced. In this case, we can only advise that the contractor/builder should add to his basic contract price sufficient monies to cover his financing expenses during the course of the contract.

6) Include everything in the written document that was agreed upon during the negotiation period. If the written contract is unclear, others (a jury or arbitration board) will decide what you meant in the contract. This is clearly not in the best interest of any party to the contract. With respect to arbitration, the MBDA "Code of Business Practices" provides a mechanism for initiating and conducting arbitration between customers and Builder/Contractor Members of the Association. Consideration should be given to incorporating this arbitration mechanism in the contract.

7) Look for signs of bad faith in the other party early in the negotiation process. If what was essentially agreed to on Monday requires drastic revision on Tuesday, this is a clear indication that "down the road," contract disputes will be inevitable.

8) Since people are not perfect, the perfect contract has yet to be written. As a result, the likelihood of a dispute always exists. Therefore, it is essential to treat each contractual obligation as if a lawsuit is likely to occur. Thus, a thorough job of

record keeping is essential. This includes recording minutes of meetings, sending memos of changes required (or ordered), taking pictures, etc. The more likely the lawsuit, the more detailed the record keeping should be.

Contractor/Manufacturer Agreement

This is the agreement whereby the manufacturer agrees to supply the builder with the metal building system which the builder will erect for the owner. This contract varies markedly between the various manufacturers, and as a result, it is not possible to state *exactly* what is included in any one document.

There are certain basic concepts, however, which seem to be common to most builder/manufacturer contracts. These include a commitment on the part of the manufacturer to supply the builder with materials, in exchange for payment according to a prescribed schedule. The builder agrees to promote the manufacturer's product. In addition, the manufacturer may also provide technical data and training for the builder.

Warranties and Guarantees

Most construction contracts must conform, in part, to certain provisions of the "Uniform Commercial Code" (UCC), which governs the sale of goods in most states, and which varies somewhat from state to state. Contracts may not conflict with provisions of the UCC. An important aspect of the UCC provisions relates to the concept of a "warranty." When goods or services are sold, an *implied warranty* exists.

At the outset, it is essential to point out that the contractor may not be providing a *guaranty*. A guaranty (guarantee) is that responsibility for fixing or repairing defective products or defective work (and, perhaps, reimbursing for losses caused by such defects) *given to a third party*. The most common form of guaranty is the "Surety Bond," where a bonding company "guarantees" the work of the contractor to the owner.

A "warranty," on the other hand, is that taking of responsibility by the principal for his own goods or services. Thus, a manufacturer warrants his product, but a contractor guarantees the materials, and warrants his workmanship. The distinction is subtle but important. In this context, the courts have held that the contractor is responsible for defective work through a statute of limitations period, even though the contract may provide for a "one year guarantee period."

The contractor's obligations during the "correction period" are as broad and inclusive as it is possible to incur. In certain instances, it is desirable to *extend* the period of responsibility to protect the owner. (An example of such an instance would relate to an item like roofing.) Specifications often require such commercial warranties. The Uniform Commercial Code requires that the goods sold must be of fair or average quality, and be able to be used for the purpose for which they are sold. To obtain maximum legal protection of a commercial warranty, the supplier should be told (in the project specifications) that the buyer is relying upon the supplier's skill; and therefore, the supplier picks up added responsibility. On the other hand, if the owner selects a brand name item, the *owner* then assumes much more responsibility for the product's performance.

Lien Concepts

A "lien" is a claim that a contractor or supplier has against real property, for goods or services supplied, for which payment has not been received. The filing of a lien is a complex legal process that varies from state to state, and involves statutory notification procedures and prescribed format.

A lien establishes a contractor as more than a general creditor, and may entitle the lien holder to first payment. A lien clouds the title to property, and creates major problems in the event financing is required. Clearly, the contractor wants to maintain the "claim" to the property until payment is received. Once this payment is received, a "lien release" is filed, in which the claim against the property is given up.

It is common (and poor) practice in many areas to have the contractor sign a lien release or a "lien waiver," thereby giving up the claim or, in fact, the *right* to file a lien *prior to being paid*. The procedure is that the check is written after the waiver is received. The lending institutions have promulgated this procedure. It is wrong, and should not be followed. Ideally, the lien waiver (or release) should not be given until payment is received—i.e., until any uncertified check has cleared. If the lending agency is insistent upon having a waiver instantly, then the only possible procedure is to either physically exchange checks for waivers, or to use a third party "escrow," who will collect both waivers and checks, and issue them when both have been received. It can not be emphasized too strongly that to turn over a lien waiver, prior to receiving payment, is poor business practice. While, in many instances, reputable owners and financial institutions can operate in such a manner, and no problems ever result, the contractor is the party taking the chance. If the risk is recognized and accepted, then the contractor is to blame if problems ensue.

Bonds

A bond of the type domestically utilized in the construction industry is a written guarantee by a third party to a construction contract, called the "surety" or "bonding company," to pay or arrange for completion of work by the "bonded" contractor in the event of default. There are three types of bonds commonly encountered in construction:

- Bid Bonds
- Performance Bonds
- Labor and Material Bonds

Bid Bonds

A bid bond is a guarantee by the surety, that the low bidder on the project will enter into a contract to do the work. The purpose of the bid bond is to prevent a bidder (who sees that his bid is much lower than the second bidder, i.e. "a lot has been left on the table"), from backing out. The bonding company must arrange for construction at the low bid price, or pay the difference between the low bid and the next low bid.

Performance Bonds

This bond guarantees that once a contract has been issued, the contractor will carry out the work to completion. In the event of default, the surety is required to arrange for completion of the work.

Labor and Material Payment Bonds

When a general contractor receives payment from the owner, there is no guarantee that the contractor will use those funds to pay for materials purchased, subcontractors, or labor. In the event the contractor does not pay his obligations, these various subcontractors and material suppliers have lien rights against the project. The surety is obligated to pay these labor and material suppliers on behalf of the owner to preclude this from happening.

It is important to recognize that when bonds are required to be utilized, the bonding company practice is simply *not* to immediately write a check to solve the problem. Experience shows that enforcement of bond requirements is complex, with the bonding company doing what it can to minimize its loss. Also, many successful and prominent contractors may be of such financial "quality" that bonds may not be required. A common procedure is to specify that bonds *may* be required in a project. If the successful low bidder (in non-government projects) is a contractor of substantial means, and an excellent track record, bonding may, in fact, not be required. Bond premiums can be paid by the owner (and not required in the bid), when bonds are then actually used.

The more established builder/contractor, who has a "track record" of years of successful experience in projects of the same (or smaller) general size than the one under immediate consideration, naturally considers bonding as a needless owner expense. On the other hand, architects and owners frequently look towards bonds as additional security, and insist on bonding.

11
Specifying Metal Building Systems

Role of the Specification

Specifications, when properly used, should supplement and complement engineering and architectural drawings, and provide information to prospective contractors on aspects of a project which cannot be described in drawings. Ideally, specifications should not duplicate information on drawings, and vice versa.

There are as many ways to write specifications about metal building systems as there are specification writers. Moreover, it is difficult (if not impossible) to write a general specification which can be used for any project. That is not the intent of this chapter. Rather, the intent is to provide certain guide specification sections for metal building systems which can generally be used for most types of projects.

The specifications which follow are the "Recommended Guide Specifications," developed by the Metal Building Manufacturers Association. The guide specification is a *performance* type specification which effectively requires that certain minimum standards for materials be met, and that the completed structure be capable of supporting certain required design loads in accordance with provisions of nationally recognized specifications (e.g., AISC, AISI, AWS, etc.)

It is, of course, possible to specify metal building systems in a proprietary manner by selecting a manufacturer, a style (or model), and an identifying number or code. This is analogous to selecting a particular car, and all of the options desired. Once this decision is made, the buyer gets precisely what he wants, and also, precisely what the auto maker has. Use of a performance specification enables the buyer to state only in "general terms" what he wants, since many manufacturers will be able to meet a guide specification, yet the finished product of each would look somewhat different.

Recommended Guide Specifications for Metal Building Systems

(The following specifications are designed as a guide for use in the preparation of contract document specifications for metal building systems.)

1. Scope

This specification covers the design, material, fabrication, and shipment of the metal building system. The system is to include the primary and secondary members, coverings, and accessories indicated in the contract documents.

2. Description of Metal Building Systems

2.01 Building Size — (Insert nominal length, width, and eave height of building. Refer to contract drawings if applicable.)

2.02 Building Type — (Insert manufacturers' typical framing designation, single or multi-span frame, roof slope, bay spacing, and endwall type, i.e., expandable or non-expandable, clear span or post and beam.)

2.03 Building Loading — (Insert the required live load, wind load, seismic load, collateral load, and auxiliary load. For crane loads, indicate type of crane, i.e., monorail, bridge, underhung, independent, etc. Also indicate wheel loads, wheel spacing, and weight of trolley and hoist.)

3. Applicable Standards and Specifications

3.01 Metal Building Systems Manual

3.1.1 "Design Practices Manual"

3.1.2 "Code of Standard Practices"

3.02 American Institute of Steel Construction (AISC).
Only those sections of "Specification for the Design, Fabrication, and Erection of Structural Steel for Buildings" relating to design requirements or allowable stresses.

3.03 American Iron and Steel Institute (AISI).
Only those section of the "Specification for the Design of Cold-Formed Steel Structural Members" and "Design of Light Gauge Steel Diaphragms" relating to design requirements and allowable stresses.

3.04 American Welding Society (AWS).
Only those sections of the "Standard Code for Arc & Gas Welding in Building Construction" relating to welding procedures.

3.05 Aluminum Association
Only those sections of the "Specification for Aluminum Structures" or "Aluminum Formed Sheet Building Sheathing Design Guide" relating to design requirements or allowable stresses.

3.06 (Insert local or model code if applicable.)

4. Design Criteria

4.01 Metal building system shall be designed for the loads indicated in the specifications and contract drawings. Application of load shall be in accordance with MBMA "Design Practices Manual."

4.02 (Insert the plans, design calculations, and certification desired. See the MBMA "Code of Standard Practice" for options.)

5. Material and Fabrication

5.01 All structural and covering materials shall be new, and meet or exceed the physical design requirements.

5.02 All structural steel to be prime painted to protect material for a short period of time in ordinary atmospheric conditions. The prime paint is to be manufacturers' standards. Cleaning of steel shall be manufacturers' standards.

5.03 All fabrication workmanship shall meet or exceed the fabrication tolerances as published by MBMA.

6. Covering

6.01 Roof Type — (Insert the type of roof system to be used, i.e., screwed-on panel, standing seam, or built-up. Indicate UL uplift classification, if required.)

6.02 Roof Finish — (Insert whether the roof will be unpainted, galvanized, aluminum coated, zinc-aluminum coated or film laminated, etc., or painted to manufacturers' standards. Special performance requirements should be indicated if applicable. Color will be selected from manufacturers' standards.)

6.03 Roof Fastening — To be in accordance with manufacturers' standards for the type of roof selected.

6.04 Wall Type — (Insert the type of wall system to be used, i.e., exposed, semi-concealed or concealed fasteners, factory or field insulated, and general appearance desired.)

6.05 Wall Finish — (Insert whether the finish is to be unpainted, galvanized, aluminum coated, zinc-aluminum coated, film laminated, etc., or painted to manufacturers' standards. Special performance standards should be indicated, if applicable. Color to be selected from manufacturers' standards.)

6.06 Wall Fastening — To be in accordance with manufacturers' standards for the type of wall selected.

6.07 Trim and Flashing — To be the type and finish in accordance with manufacturers' standards.

6.08 Mastic to be furnished and installed in accordance with the recommendations of the manufacturer.

7. Accessories

(Insert the applicable accessories required for the project that are to be included in the metal building system. Accessories to be selected from manufacturers' standard offerings.)

7.01 Personnel Doors

7.02 Windows

7.03 Overhead Type doors

7.04 Ventilators

7.05 Louvers

7.06 Skylights and Wall-lights

7.07 Insulation (Indicate the "U" value performance of the building envelope.)

7.08 Sliding Doors

8. Erection and Installation

Unloading instructions, storage of materials, and erection procedures as outlined and recommended by the building manufacturer shall be followed as closely as possible and, together with accepted trade practices, shall conform to details and instruction as shown on the erection or assembly drawings. Erection tolerances are those set forth in AISC "Code of Standard Practice," except individual members are considered plumb, level, and aligned if the error does not exceed 1:300.

9. Drawings

Proposal drawings, when required, clearly indicating the scope of work, along with the proposal shall be considered as sufficient information for bidding documents.

After the contract is awarded, applicable erection drawings and instructions shall be available prior to shipment of material.

10. Certification

When required by the terms of the contract, the manufacturer furnishes design calculations or a letter of certification signed and sealed by a registered professional engineer for the structural framing and covering panels of the metal building system(s). Such design calculations may be manual or by electronic computer, at the discretion of the metal building system manufacturer.

Sample Specifications for Metal Building Systems

Since many metal building systems contractors also serve as general contractors, this book includes sample specifications for basic sections which would routinely exist in metal building system projects. These include the following sections:

Division 1

Section 1300   Submittals and Substitutions
Section 1400   Testing Laboratory Services
Section 1500   Temporary Facilities and Controls
Section 1550   Survey

Division 2

Section 2010   Subsurface Conditions

Section 2200   Excavation, Filling, and Grading

Division 3

Section 3200   Concrete Reinforcement

Section 3300   Cast-in-Place Concrete

The sections are developed in the three part format of the "Construction Specifications Institute," where Part 1 of each section deals with general aspects such as work included, quality control, references, applicable codes, testing procedures, etc. Part 2 provides a detailed description of every material to be used as a part of the work of that section, and Part 3 describes installation procedures for every material or product described in Part 2.

Part 1.00 — GENERAL

1.01 Description:

A. Work included:

1. Wherever possible throughout the Contract Documents, the minimum acceptable quality of workmanship and materials has been defined, either by manufacturer's name and catalog number, or by reference to recognized industry standards.

2. To ensure that the specified products are furnished and installed in accordance with design intent, procedures have been established for advance submittal of design data, and for its review and approval or rejection by the Designer.

B. Related work described elsewhere:

1. Contractual requirement for submittals:
   General Conditions and Supplementary Conditions

2. Individual submittals required:
   Pertinent sections of these Specifications

1.02 Product Handling:

Make all submittals of Shop Drawings, samples, requests for substitutions, and other items, in strict accordance with the provisions of this Section of these Specifications.

Part 2.00 — PRODUCTS

2.01 Shop Drawings:

A. Scale required:

Unless otherwise specifically directed by the Designer, make all Drawings of a sufficient scale in order that the Drawings show all pertinent features of the item, and its method of connection to the work.

B. Type of prints required:

Unless otherwise specifically directed by the Designer, make

all Shop Drawing prints in blue or black line on white
background.

  C. Number of prints required:

Submit all Shop Drawings in the quantity which is required
to be returned, plus two copies which will be retained by
the Designer.

2.04 Substitutions

  A. Designer's approval required:

    1. The Contract is based on the materials, equipment, and
methods described in the Contract Documents.

    2. The Designer will consider proposals for substitution of
materials, equipment, and methods, only when such proposals are accompanied by full and complete technical
data, and all other information required by the Designer
to evaluate the proposed substitution.

    3. Do not substitute materials, equipment, or methods unless
such substitution has been specifically approved for this
work by the Designer.

  B. "Or equal":

    1. Where the phrase "or equal" or "or equal as approved by
the Designer" occurs in the Contract Documents, do not
assume that material, equipment, or methods will be
approved as equal by the Designer, unless the item has been
specifically approved for this work by the Designer.

    2. The decision of the Designer shall be final.

  C. Availability of specified items:

    1. Verify, prior to bidding, that all specified items will be
available in time for installation during orderly and timely
progress of the work.

    2. In the event specified item or items will not be so available,
notify the Designer prior to receipt of bids.

    3. Costs of delays because of non-availability of specified
items, when such delays could have been avoided by the
Contractor, will be backcharged as necessary, and shall not
be borne by the Owner.

  D. Separate substitute bids:

Bidders may, if they wish, submit completely separate bids

using materials and methods other than those described in these Contract Documents, provided that all substitutions are clearly identified and described, and that the bid is in all other respects in accordance with the provisions of the Contract Documents.

Part 3.00 — EXECUTION

3.01 Identification of Submittals:

Completely identify each submittal and resubmittal by showing at least the following information:

A. Name and address of submitter, plus name and telephone number of the individual who may be contacted for further information.

B. Name of project.

C. Drawing number and Specifications Section number to which the submittal applies.

D. Whether this is an original submittal or resubmittal.

3.02 Coordination of Submittals:

A. General:

Prior to submittal for Designer's review, use all means necessary to fully coordinate all material, including the following procedures:

1. Determine and verify all field dimensions and conditions, materials, catalog numbers, and similar data.

2. Coordinate as required with all trades and with all public agencies involved.

3. Secure all necessary approvals from public agencies and others, and signify by stamp, or other means, that they have been secured.

4. Clearly indicate all deviations from the Contract Documents.

B. Grouping of submittals:

Unless otherwise specifically permitted by the Designer, make all submittals in groups containing all associated items; the Designer may reject partial submittals, as not complying with the provisions of the Contract Documents.

3.03 Timing of Submittals:

   A. General:

   1. Make all submittals far enough in advance of scheduled dates of installation to provide all required time for reviews, for securing necessary approvals, for possible revision and resubmittal, and for placing orders and securing delivery.

   2. In scheduling, allow at least three full working days for the Designer's review following his receipt of the submittal.

   B. Delays:

   Costs of delays occasioned by tardiness of submittals may be backcharged as necessary, and shall not be borne by the Owner.

Part 1.00 — GENERAL

1.01 Description:

A. Work included:

From time to time during progress of the work, the Owner may require that testing be performed to determine that materials provided for the work meet the specified requirements; such testing includes, but is not necessarily limited to:

1. Soil compaction

2. Cast-in-place concrete

B. Related work described elsewhere:

Requirements for testing may be described in various sections of the Specifications; where no testing requirements are described, but the Owner decides that testing is required, the Owner may require testing to be performed under current, pertinent standards for testing.

C. Work not included:

1. Selection of testing laboratory:

The Owner will select a pre-qualified, independent testing laboratory.

2. Payment for initial testing services:

The Owner will pay for all initial services of the testing laboratory, as further described in Article 2.01 of this Section of these Specifications.

1.02 Quality Assurance:

A. Qualifications of testing laboratory:

The testing laboratory will be qualified to the Owner's approval in accordance with ASTM E-329-70 "Recommended Practice for Inspection and Testing Agencies for Concrete and Steel Used in Construction."

B. Codes and standards:

Testing, when required, will be in accordance with all pertinent codes and regulations, and with selected standards of the American Society for Testing and Materials.

1.03 Product Handling:

Promptly process and distribute all required copies of test reports and related instructions to ensure all necessary retesting and/or replacement of materials with the least possible delay in progress of the work.

Part 2.00 — PRODUCTS

2.01 Payment for Testing Services:

A. Initial services:

1. The Owner will pay for all initial testing services requested by the Owner.

2. When initial tests indicate non-compliance with the Contract Documents, the costs of initial tests associated with that non-compliance will be deducted by the Owner from the Contract Sum.

B. Retesting:

When initial tests indicate non-compliance with the Contract Documents, all subsequent retesting occasioned by the non-compliance shall be performed by the same testing laboratory, and the costs thereof will be deducted by the Owner from the Contract Sum.

2.02 Code Compliance Testing:

Inspections and tests required by codes or ordinances, or by a plan approval authority, and made by a legally constituted authority, shall be the responsibility of, and shall be paid for by the Contractor, unless otherwise provided in the Contract Documents.

2.03 Contractor's Convenience Testing:

Inspection or testing performed exclusively for the Contractor's convenience shall be the sole responsibility of the Contractor.

Part 3.00 — EXECUTION

3.01 Cooperation with Testing Laboratory:

Representatives of the testing laboratory shall have access to the work at all times; provide facilities for such access in order that the laboratory may properly perform its functions.

3.02   Schedules for Testing:

   A.   Establishing schedule:

     1.   By advance discussion with the testing laboratory selected by the Owner, determine the time required for the laboratory to perform its test and to issue each of its findings.

     2.   Provide all required time within the construction schedule.

   B.   Revising schedule:

   When changes of construction schedule are necessary during construction, coordinate all such changes of schedule with the testing laboratory as required.

   C.   Adherence to schedule:

   When the testing laboratory is ready to test according to the determined schedule, but is prevented from testing or taking specimens due to incompleteness of the work, all extra costs for testing attributable to the delay may be backcharged to the Contractor, and shall not be borne by the Owner.

3.03   Taking Specimens:

All specimens and samples for testing, unless otherwise provided in these Contract Documents, will be taken by the testing laboratory; all sampling equipment and personnel will be provided by the testing laboratory; and all deliveries of specimens and samples to the testing laboratory will be performed by the testing laboratory.

Part 1.00 — GENERAL

1.01 Description

    A. Work included:

    Temporary facilities and controls required for this work include, but are not necessarily limited to:

      1. Temporary utilities such as gas, water, electricity, and telephone.

      2. Field offices and sheds.

      3. Sanitary facilities.

      4. Enclosures such as tarpaulins, barricades, and canopies.

      5. A project sign.

      6. Fencing of the construction area.

      7. Haul road.

    B. Related work described elsewhere:

      1. Compliance with safety regulations:

      Compliance with all requirements of pertinent regulations is described in the General Conditions of the Contract.

      2. Subcontractor equipment:

      Except that equipment furnished by subcontractors shall comply with all requirements of pertinent safety regulations, the ladders, hoists, planks, and similar items normally furnished by individual trades in execution of their own portions of the work are not part of this Section of these Specifications.

      3. Utility hook-up:

      Installation and hook-up of the various utility lines are described in the pertinent other sections of these Specifications.

1.02 Product Handling

A. Protection:

Use all means necessary to maintain temporary facilities and controls in proper and safe condition throughout progress of the work.

B. Replacements:

In the event of loss or damage, immediately make all repairs and replacements necessary to the approval of the Engineer, and at no additional cost to the Owner.

Part 2.00 — PRODUCTS

2.01 Utilities:

A. Temporary utilities:

1. General:

Provide and pay all costs for all gas, water, and electricity required for the performance of the work.

2. Temporary gas and water:

Furnish and install all necessary temporary piping and, upon completion of the work, remove all such temporary piping. After water has been made available at the building, and a permanent meter has been installed, the Owner will pay all costs of water consumed.

3. Temporary electricity:

a. Furnish and install all necessary temporary wiring.

b. Furnish and install area distribution boxes, so located that the individual trades may use their own construction-type extension cords to obtain adequate power and artificial lighting at all points where required by inspectors and for safety.

4. Temporary heat:

a. Contractor will furnish and pay for all costs for temporary heat until such time as the permanent heating system can be put into operation in the normal construction process.

b. Contractor shall pay all costs of fuel and/or electricity for the operation of temporary heating.

B. Telephone:

Maintain in the job office a telephone for the use of the Designer; the telephone may be coin operated.

2.02 Field Office and Sheds:

Furnish and install a field office building adequate in size and accommodation for all Contractor's offices, superintendent's offince, supply and tool room; make the field office available to the Designer throughout the entire construction period.

2.03 Sanitary Facilities:

Furnish and install all required temporary toilet buildings with sanitary toilets for use of all workmen; comply with all minimum requirements of the Health Department or other public agency having jurisdiction; maintain in a sanitary condition at all times. No other toilets on the site shall be used until permanent facilities in the building are available.

2.04 Enclosures:

Furnish, install, and maintain for the duration of construction all required scaffolds, tarpaulins, barricades, canopies, warning signs, steps, bridges, platforms, and other temporary construction necessary for proper completion of the work in compliance with all pertinent safety and other regulations.

2.05 Project Sign:

Furnish and install a project sign as indicated on the Drawings; all lettering shall be performed by a journeyman sign painter; allow no other sign or advertising of any type on job site, except as specifically approved by the Designer. Sign shall be removed from the site by the Contractor at project completion.

2.06 Fencing of the Construction Area:

A. General:

Furnish and install a temporary fence around the entire construction area as indicated on the Drawings.

B. Construction:

The temporary fence shall consist of woven wire mesh, not less than six feet in height, complete with metal or wood posts and all required bracing, and with truck and pedestrian gates as indicated on the Drawings.

2.07   **Haul Road:**

Prior to completion of paved areas on the site, confine all on-site vehicular traffic to the haul road location shown on the Drawings.

Part 3.00 — EXECUTION

3.01   **Removal:**

Maintain all temporary facilities and controls as long as needed for the safe and proper completion of the work; remove all such temporary facilities and controls as rapidly as progress of the work will permit or as directed by the Designer.

Division 1
Survey
Section 1550

Part 1.00 — GENERAL

A. The owner has a property survey which has been utilized in establishing grades, setbacks, location of structures, and utilities. Such a survey does not form a part of these Contract Documents, and is not guaranteed in any way.

B. The Contractor shall retain the services of a registered surveyor to lay out building lines and grades for the work, to insure that the structures are properly located on the site.

C. As the work proceeds, the work of prior construction shall be checked in terms of location and elevation (e.g., locations of anchor bolts, fastenings, bearing surfaces, holding devices, etc.). Notify the Designer of any discrepancies, and do not proceed with any of the work until adjustments have been approved by the Designer.

Parts 2.00 and 3.00 do not apply to this Section.

Part 1.00 — GENERAL

1.01 Description:

Soil borings have been taken by:

A copy of the boring logs may be obtained at:

The Office of the Designer.

The report was obtained only for the Owner's use in the design and is not a part of the Contract Documents. The report and log of borings is available for Contractor's information, but is not a warrant of subsurface conditions.

1.02 Additional Information:

The Contractor should visit the site, and acquaint himself with all existing conditions. Prior to bidding, bidders may make their own subsurface investigations to satisfy themselves as to site and subsurface conditions, but such subsurface investigations shall be performed only under time schedules and arrangements approved in advance by the Designer.

1.03 Quality Assurance:

A Soil Engineer may be retained by the Owner to observe performance of work in connection with excavating, filling, and grading. Readjust all work performed that does not meet technical or design requirements, but make no deviations from the Contract Documents without specific and written approval of the Designer.

Division 2
Excavating, Filling,
And Grading
Section 2200

Part 1.00 — GENERAL

1.01 Description:

   A. Work included:

   Excavating, filling, and grading required for this work includes, but is not necessarily limited to:

    1. Excavating for footings and foundations.

    2. Filling and backfilling to attain indicated grades.

    3. Rough and finish grading of the site.

    4. Furnishing and installing granular base course under all interior concrete slabs on grade.

   B. Related work described elsewhere:

    1. Testing laboratory services: Section 1400

    2. Subsurface conditions: Section 2010

1.02 Job Conditions

   A. Dust Control:

    1. Use all means necessary to control dust on and near the work, and on and near all off-site borrow areas, if such dust is caused by the Contractor's operations during performance of the work, or if resulting from the conditions in which the Contractor leaves the site.

    2. Thoroughly moisten all surfaces as required to prevent dust from being a nuisance to the public, neighbors, and concurrent performance of other work on the site.

   B. Protection:

    1. Use all means necessary to protect all materials of this Section before, during, and after installation, and to protect all objects designated to remain.

    2. Particular care shall be taken to avoid damage to any and all marked, as well as unmarked, underground utility

lines, storm drainage lines, and piping. Notify all companies or governing bodies owning pipes, conduits, and overhead systems if questions or problems arise. Keep drainage ways open. Provide bracing necessary to support adjoining soil, structures, and underground piping and conduits.

3. In the event of damage, immediately make all repairs and replacements necessary to the approval of the Designer, and at no additional cost to the Owner.

4. Provide and maintain planking and protection for walks, curbs, drains, and trees and boxing around corners of building walls to prevent damage by trucking, grading, and other operations.

Part 2.00 — PRODUCTS

2.01 Fill Material, General:

A. Approval required:

All fill material shall be submitted to the Designer for review as to suitability. Acceptance by Designer in no way eliminates or reduces the Contractor's obligation to meet performance standards contained in these Specifications.

B. Notification:

For approval of imported fill material, notify the Designer at least four working days in advance of intention to import material, designate the proposed borrow area, and permit the Designer to sample as necessary for the borrow area for the purpose of making acceptance tests to prove the quality of the material.

C. All testing and review of fill materials will be done by the soil testing laboratory selected by the Designer.

2.02 Fill Materials

A. "General fill" for filling and backfilling all areas outside of the building lines (except for backfill against walls) may be broken stone, sand, bank-run gravel, earth, or approved material from excavation. All such fill shall be free from peat, wood, large stones or boulders, roots, cinders, trash, or other similar objectionable material with maximum size of rocks, or lumps, not more than 6".

B. "Select fill" for fill under footings, structures, backfill against walls, and "inside" building up to 6" beneath the underside of floor slabs shall be a coarse grained, cohesionless soil with less than 5% passing the No. 200 sieve. The material shall be free of peat, loam, wood, and other foreign material with maximum size of rocks or lumps not more than 1½".

C. "Drainage fill" for use as a "base course" under all concrete slabs-on-grade, interior floor slabs and exterior walks, steps, etc., shall be as shown or 6" minimum, thick bed of compacted, granular, free-draining fill material consisting of clean bank-run gravel, sand, or crushed stone of full range of sizes. Maximum clay content not to exceed 5%. Maximum size of aggregate to be ¾".

Part 3.00 — EXECUTION

3.01 General:

A. Familiarization:

1. Prior to all work of this Section, become thoroughly familiar with the site, the site conditions, and all portions of the work falling within this Section.

2. All work of this Section shall be performed in proper sequence, so as to advance the work in the best interest of overall job progress and minimum interference of the various trades.

B. Backfilling prior to approvals:

1. Do not allow, or cause, any work performed or installed to be covered up, or enclosed, by work of this Section prior to all required inspections, tests, and approvals.

2. Should any of the work be so enclosed, or covered up, before it has been approved, uncover all such work at no additional cost to the Owner.

3. After the work has been completely tested, inspected, and approved, make all repairs and replacements necessary to restore the work to the condition in which it was found at the time of uncovering, all at no additional cost to the Owner.

3.02 Finish Elevations and Lines

All excavation shall be done using the horizontal and vertical control established by the project surveyor.

3.03 Excavating:

A. Depressions resulting from removal of obstructions:

Where depressions result from, or have resulted from, the removal of surface or subsurface obstructions, open the depression to equipment working width, and remove all debris and soft material as directed by the Designer.

B. Other areas:

1. Excavate to grades shown on the Drawings.

2. Where excavation grades are not shown on the Drawings, excavate as required to accommodate the installation with full allowance for fill under slabs and pavements. All exterior footings shall be carried to frost depth, as defined by local building code, unless shown otherwise on the Drawings, whether or not they are so shown on the Drawings. Excavations shall be level and to exact depths, dimensions, and shapes indicated on Drawings so that footings bear on firm, level soil. Level off bottoms of all excavations.

C. Overexcavation:

Backfill and compact all overexcavated areas as specified for fill below, and at no additional cost to the Owner.

D. Frost protection:

Protect bottom of excavation from frost. Do not backfill or place foundations, footings, or slabs on frozen ground.

E. Excess excavation:

Excavated material in excess of that required for backfill around the building shall be wasted off-site by the Contractor. Additional material required for grading and backfilling will be furnished by the Contractor as required.

3.04 Preparation of Subgrade:

A. Scarifying:

After the site has been cleared, stripped, and excavated to within six inches of the specified depths for recompaction, scarify the exposed surface to a minimum depth of six inches, thoroughly moisture-condition, and compact to the requirements specified for fill below.

B. Leveling:

Remove all ruts, hummocks, and other uneven surfaces by surface grading prior to placement of fill.

C. Subgrade elevations:

1. Subgrade for general fill to be 6″ below finished grade.

2. Subgrade for select fill to be to the underside of footings and to within 6″ of the underside of slabs.

3.05   Excess Water Control:

A. Unfavorable weather:

1. Do not place, spread, or roll any fill material during unfavorable weather conditions.

2. Do not resume operations until moisture content and fill density are satisfactory to the Engineer.

B. Flooding:

Provide berms or channels to prevent flooding of subgrade; promptly remove all water collecting in depressions.

C. Softened subgrade:

Where soil has been softened or eroded by flooding or placement during unfavorable weather, remove all damaged areas and recompact as specified for fill and compaction below.

D. Dewatering:

1. Provide and maintain at all times during construction, ample means and devices with which to promptly remove and dispose of all water from every source entering the excavations or other parts of the work. Do not conduct or drain water to adjoining properties without written approval of the Designer.

2. Dewater by means which will ensure dry excavations and the preservation of the final lines and grades of bottoms of excavations.

3.06   Fill and Compaction:

A. Filling:

After subgrade compaction has been approved by the De-

signer, spread approved fill material in layers not exceeding 8"
in uncompacted thickness.

1. Fill all areas outside of buildings, slabs, and paving which
   receive planting and seeding with general fill.

2. Fill all areas under footings, slabs, paving, and behind
   retaining walls with select fill. Extend the select fill outside
   of the footing or slab limit a distance equal to the depth
   of excavation.

3. Fill below concrete slabs: after the subgrade preparation
   work, and all required filling, compacting, and rough
   grading work to bring subgrade to proper alignment and
   cross section has been completed, provide a 6" layer of
   drainage fill under all interior and exterior slabs and walks.

4. Filling and backfilling shall be done carefully, so as to
   avoid damage to foundations, walls, pipes, conduits, etc.
   Filling shall be done evenly on both sides of pipes and wall
   to avoid wedging or eccentric action.

B. Moisture-conditioning:

Water or aerate the fill material as necessary, and thoroughly
mix to obtain a moisture content which will permit proper
compaction in accordance with specified compaction procedures.

C. Compaction, general:

Compact each soil layer to at least the specified minimum
degree; repeat compaction process until plan grade is attained.

D. Degree of compaction requirements:

1. General fill to be compacted at optimum moisture content
   to 85% maximum density, as determined in accordance with
   ASTM D1557 Method D (modified Proctor).

2. Select fill and drainage fill shall be placed in 8" layers at
   optimum moisture content, and compacted to 95% maximum density, as determined in accordance with ASTM
   D1557 Method D (modified Proctor) or 70% relative density
   as determined by ASTM D2049.

3.07 Excavating for Footings:

A. Preparation:

1. To minimize differential settlement, it is essential that

earth surfaces upon which footing will be placed be compacted to the approval of the Engineer, and in accordance
with the compaction requirements established in this Section of these Specifications.

2. Verify that all compaction is complete and approved prior
   to excavating for footings.

B. Excavation:

1. Cut off bottom of trenches level, and remove all loose soil.

2. Where soft spots are encountered, remove all defective
   material and replace with lean concrete or crushed stone
   subject to approval of the Engineer.

3.10   Placing Granular Cushion:

Carefully place the granular drainage-fill cushion in areas to
receive concrete slabs-on-grade, uniformly attaining the thickness indicated on the Drawings, and providing all required
transition planes.

Part 1.00 — GENERAL

1.01 Description:

A. Work included:

Furnish and install all reinforcement and associated items required and/or indicated on the Drawings for all cast-in-place concrete.

B. Related work described elsewhere:

1. Placement of other embedded items: Section 3300.

1.02 Quality Assurance:

A. Qualifications of workmen:

Provide at least one person who shall be present at all times during execution of this portion of the work, and who shall be thoroughly familiar with the type of materials being installed, and the best methods for their installation, and who shall direct all work performed under this Section.

B. Codes, standards, and publications:

1. In addition to complying with all pertinent codes and regulations, comply with all pertinent recommendations contained in "Manual of Standard Practice for Detailing Reinforced Concrete Structures," publication ACI 315-65 of the American Concrete Institute.

2. Where provisions of pertinent codes and standards conflict with this Specification, the more stringent provisions shall govern.

1.03 Submittals:

A. Shop Drawings:

1. Within 35 days after award of Contract, and before any concrete reinforcement materials are delivered to the job site, submit Shop Drawings to the Designer in accordance with Section 1300 of these Specifications.

2. Do not deliver concrete reinforcement to the job site until receipt of Shop Drawings' approval from the Designer.

B. Samples and certificates:

Provide all data and access required for testing as described in Section 1400 of these Specifications.

1.04 Product Handling:

A. Protection:

1. Use all means necessary to protect concrete reinforcement before, during, and after installation, and to protect the installed work and materials of all other trades.

2. Store in a manner to prevent excessive rusting and fouling with dirt, grease, and other bond-breaking coatings.

3. Use all necessary precautions to maintain identification after the bundles are broken.

B. Replacements:

In the event of damage, immediately make all repairs and replacements necessary to the approval of the Designer, and at no additional cost to the Owner.

Part 2.00 — PRODUCTS

2.01 Concrete Reinforcement:

All concrete reinforcement materials shall be new, free from rust, and complying with the following reference standards.

A. Bars: "Specification for Deformed Billet-Steel Bars for Concrete Reinforcement," ASTM A-615, grade as noted on the plans.

B. Wire: "Specifications for Cold-Drawn Steel Wire for Concrete Reinforcement," ASTM A-82.

C. Wire Fabric: "Specifications for Wire Fabric for Concrete Reinforcement," ASTM A-185.

2.02 Other Materials:

All other materials, not specifically described but required for a complete and proper installation of concrete reinforcement, shall be selected by the Contractor subject to the approval of the Designer.

Part 1.00 — GENERAL

1.01 Description:

A. Work included:

Cast-in-place concrete including forming required for this work is indicated on the Drawings and includes, but is not necessarily limited to:

1. Footings and foundations.
2. Slabs-on-grade.
3. Piers, walls, and grade beams.
4. Concrete curbs.

B. Related work described elsewhere:

1. Concrete reinforcement: Section 3200.
2. Testing lab services: Section 1400.
3. Excavation: Section 2200.

1.02 Quality Assurance:

A. Qualifications of workmen:

1. Provide at least one person who shall be present at all times during execution of this portion of the work, and who shall be thoroughly trained and experienced in placing the types of concrete specified, and who shall direct all work performed under this Section.
2. For finishing of exposed surfaces of the concrete, use only thoroughly trained and experienced journeyman concrete finishers.

B. Codes, standards, and publications:

1. In addition to complying with all pertinent codes and regulations, comply with all pertinent recommendations of "Structural Concrete for Buildings," publication ACI 301-66 of the American Concrete Institute.

2. Where provisions of pertinent codes and standards conflict with this Specification, the more stringent provisions shall govern.

1.03 Submittals:

A. Materials list:

Within 35 days after award of Contract, and before any concrete is delivered to the job site, submit to the Designer, in accordance with Section 1300 of these Specifications, a complete list of all materials proposed to be furnished and installed under this portion of the work, showing manufacturer's name and catalog number of all items such as admixtures, and the name and address of transit-mix concrete suppliers.

B. Transit-mix delivery slips:

1. Keep a record at the job site, showing time and place of each pour of concrete, together with transit-mix delivery slip certifying contents of the pour, including date, serial number, name of plant, job location, cement content, admixtures, maximum aggregate size, and water added at job.

2. Make the record available to the Designer for his inspection upon request.

3. Upon completion of this portion of the work, deliver the record and the delivery slips to the Designer.

1.04 Product Handling:

A. Protection:

Use all means necessary to protect cast-in-place concrete materials before, during, and after installation, and to protect the installed work and materials of all other trades.

B. Replacements:

In the event of damage; immediately make all repairs and replacements necessary to the approval of the Engineer and at no additional cost to the Owner. This particularly applies to shoring and bracing.

C. Do not use aluminum pipe if concrete is to be transported by means of pumping. Aluminum shall not be allowed in concrete.

1.05   Reference Specifications:

A. The following reference specifications, hereinafter mentioned, shall be a part of this Specification, as if herein written, and shall govern except where superseded by particular requirements of Specification.

ACI 211.1 — Recommended practice for Selecting Proportions for Normal Weight Concrete.

ACI 214 — Recommended Practice for Evaluation of Compression Test Results of Field Concrete.

ACI 301 — Specifications for Structural Concrete for Buildings.

ACI 306 — Recommended Practice for Cold Weather Concreting.

ACI 315 — Manual of Standard Practice for Detailing Reinforced Concrete Structures.

ACI 318 — Building Code Requirements for Reinforced Concrete.

ACI 305 — Recommended Practice for Hot Weather Concreting.

ACI 304 — Recommended Practice for Measuring, Mixing, and Placing Concrete.

ASTM C39 — Standard Method of Test for Compressive Strength of Molded Concrete Cylinders.

ASTM C94 — Standard Specification for Ready-Mixed Concrete.

ASTM C138 — Standard Method of Test for Weight per Cubic Foot, Yield, and Air Content (Gravimetric) of Concrete.

ASTM C143 — Standard Method of Test for Slump of Portland Cement Concrete.

ASTM C173 — Standard Method of Test for Air Content of Freshly Mixed Concrete by the Volumetric Method.

ASTM C192 — Standard Method of Making and Curing Concrete Test Specimens in the Laboratory.

ASTM C231 — Standard Method of Test for Air Content of Freshly Mixed Concrete by the Pressure Method.

B. All specifications shall be latest date.

C. ACI publications are available from American Concrete Institute, P.O. Box 4754, Redford Station, Detroit, Michigan, 48219. ASTM publications are available from American Society for Testing Materials, 1916 Race Street, Philadelphia, Pennsylvania, 19103.

Part 2.00 — PRODUCTS
2.01 Concrete:

A. General:

All concrete, unless otherwise specifically permitted by the Designer, shall be transit-mixed in accordance with ASTM C-94.

B. When specified slump is 3″ or less, tolerance plus or minus ½″. When specified slump is greater than 3″, tolerance — plus or minus 1″.

C. Cement:

All cement shall be Portland cement conforming to ASTM C-150 Type I, and shall be the product of one manufacturer; the temperature of cement delivered to the plant shall not exceed 150 degrees F.

D. Quality:

Class of concrete to be used shall be as specified on the plans. Slump and minimum cement content per cubic yard are given per 28 day strength. Slump shall be maximum permitted, but not less than 1″.

1. 4000 psi = 3″ max. slump, 570 lbs. min. cement content.
2. 3000 psi = 3″ max. slump, 470 lbs. min. cement content.

   Cement contents are noted as a minimum, and shall in no way mean that additional cement will not be required to meet specified strengths.

E. Water-cement ratios:

Maximum water-cement ratio (or minimum cement content) shall be determined from field experience with the materials to be used for this project, or from laboratory trial batches, as follows:

1. Where the concrete production facility has a record of at least 30 consecutive strength tests representing materials to be used in this project, the strength used for selecting mix proportions shall exceed the design strength by at least:

400 psi if standard deviation is less than 300 psi
550 psi if standard deviation is 300 to 400 psi
700 psi if standard deviation is 400 to 500 psi
900 psi if standard deviation is 500 to 600 psi

F. Aggregates:

Aggregates shall conform to ASTM C33. Maximum size aggregates shall not be larger than one-fifth of the narrowest dimension between form sides, one-third the depth of slabs, nor three-fourths of the minimum clear distance between reinforcing bars, or between bars and forms, whichever is least.

1. Maximum 1½″ size aggregate shall be proportioned with ¾″ aggregate to produce gradation conforming to size No. 467 in Table II of ASTM C33. 1½″ size maximum aggregate may be used in footings.

2. Maximum 1″ size aggregate shall conform to gradation size No. 57. Use where clearances are met.

3. Maximum ¾″ size aggregate shall conform to gradation size No. 67. Use where clearances are met.

4. Maximum ⅜″ size aggregate shall conform to fine aggregate gradation of ASTM C33. Use only for topping of precast and metal pan stair treads and landings.

G. Air entrained concrete:

Air entrained concrete shall be manufactured by using Type IA Portland cement meeting the requirements of ASTM C175 or ASTM approved air entraining agent. Air entrainment shall meet requirements of ACI 301. Use for exterior slabs and concrete exposed to weather. Air content to be 6%, plus or minus 1%.

H. Calcium chloride:

Calcium chloride and other admixtures shall not be used without Designer's written approval.

2.03 Testing:

A. General:

1. Routine testing of concrete materials for compliance with Specifications will be paid for by Owner. Contractor shall cooperate with Testing Laboratory to aid them in making cylinders, and other testing.

      2. Testing of field cured cylinders, testing required because of changes in materials or mix proportions, and extra testing required due to failure of concrete to meet specification requirements, shall be at the Contractor's expense.

  B. Quality control tests:

      1. Concrete samples shall be obtained in accordance with ASTM C172. Each strength test shall be from a different batch of concrete on a random basis.

      2. A strength test shall consist of four standard cylinders, with two tested at seven days, and two tested at 28 days.

      3. Strength tests shall be made for each of the following conditions: Each class of concrete; each day's pour; each 50 cubic yards of concrete or fraction thereof.

      4. Cylinders shall be made and cured in accordance with ASTM C31, and tested in accordance with ASTM C39.

      5. Slump tests shall be made of the same concrete from which strength tests are made, following the procedure in ASTM C143.

      6. When air-entrained concrete is used, air content tests shall be made of the same concrete from which strength tests are made in accordance with ASTM C231.

      7. A record shall be made by the Contractor of the delivery ticket number for each load of concrete tested, and the exact location in the work at which each load, represented by a strength test, is deposited.

      8. The Concrete Contractor shall advise the testing agency sufficiently in advance of operations to allow for completion of tests, and shall provide and maintain facilities for safe storage and proper curing of cylinders at the site for the first 24 hours, as described in ASTM C31.

  C. Evaluation of test results:

      1. To conform to the requirements of this Specification, the averages of all sets of three consecutive strength tests shall equal or exceed the specified 28 day strength, and no individual test shall fall below the specified value by more than 500 psi.

      2. If concrete fails to meet strength requirements, the Owner,

may, at his option, require any of the following actions or combination thereof, at the Contractor's expense:

- Additional curing.
- Modification to the mix proportions for the remaining concrete.
- Additional testing, including drilled cores.
- Reinforcement with additional construction.
- Removal and replacement of defective work.

Part 3.00 — EXECUTION

3.01 Surface Conditions:

A. Inspection:

1. Prior to all work of this Section, carefully inspect the installed work of all other trades, and verify that all such work is complete to the point where this installation may properly commence.

2. Verify that all items to be embedded in concrete are in place.

3. Verify that concrete may be placed to the lines and elevations indicated on the Drawings, with all required clearance from reinforcement. Use the control developed by the Project Surveyor.

B. Discrepancies:

1. In the event of discrepancy, immediately notify the Designer.

2. Do not proceed with installation in areas of discrepancy, until all such discrepancies have been fully resolved.

3.02 Notification:

The Contractor shall notify the Designer at least 24 hours prior to placing any concrete so that inspection of reinforcing may be made.

3.03 Preparation:

A. General:

1. Remove all wood scraps and debris from the areas in which concrete will be placed.

2. Thoroughly clean the areas to ensure proper placement and bonding of concrete. Reinforcing to be free from mud,

oil, or other coating that will reduce the bond.

3. Throughly wet the forms (except in freezing weather), or oil them; remove all standing water. Wet any porous subgrade, and seal any extremely porous subgrade. Oiling of forms shall be done before placing steel.

4. Thoroughly clean all transporting and handling equipment.

5. Contractor assumes full responsibility for the design of forms include centering and adequacy to meet tolerances. Forms must meet OSHA requirements.

3.04 Placing Concrete:

A. Method:

1. Convey concrete from mixer to place of final deposit by methods that will prevent separation and loss of materials.

2. For chuting, pumping, and pneumatically conveying concrete, use only equipment of such size and design as to ensure a practically continuous flow of concrete at the delivery end without loss or separation of materials.

3. Deposit concrete as nearly as possible in its final position to avoid segregation due to rehandling and flowing.

4. Place concrete as dry as possible, consistent with good workmanship, never exceeding the maximum specified slump.

5. Concrete shall be delivered to the site of work and discharged within 1½ hours or before 300 revolutions of drum or blades, whichever comes first. In hot weather, the time shall be reduced to avoid rapid setting.

6. No water shall be added on the job unless authorized by the Designer. Mixing time shall be appropriately increased when water is added.

B. Rate of placement:

1. Place concrete at such a rate that concrete is at all times plastic and flows readily between bare bars.

2. When placing is once started, carry it on as a continuous operation until placement of the panel or section is complete.

3. Do not pour a greater area at one time than can be properly

finished without checking; this is particularly important during hot or dry weather.

4. Do not, in any case, pour a slab length greater than 60 feet or area of 1200 square feet without construction joints.

C. Compaction:

1. Thorougly consolidate all concrete by suitable means during placement, working it around all embedded fixtures and into corner of forms.

2. During placement, thoroughly compact the concrete by hand tamping and by mechanical vibration.

D. Acceptability:

Do not use retempered concrete or concrete that has been contaminated by foreign materials.

3.05   Construction Joints

A. Location:

Construction joints shall conform to ACI 318-77, Section 6.4, and as located on plans.

B. Approval:

Obtain the Designer's approval of location of all construction joints and control joints in the work, prior to start of concrete placement.

3.06   Leveling and Finishing:

A. General:

1. Tamp slabs with a jitterbug to depress the rock, and then pushfloat with a bull float as necessary.

2. Take care that the wet slab meets the screeds accurately, and does not rise above or lower below them.

3. Carefully provide slab depressions as required for the finishes indicated on the Drawings.

B. Finishing:

1. Unless otherwise indicated on the Drawings, make all slabs even and uniform in appearance, and in true planes plus or minus ⅛″ in ten feet.

2. Where floor drains or floor slopes are indicated, slope slabs uniformly to provide even fall for drainage.

3. Trowel all interior slabs to a smooth, hard finish using steel trowels.

C. Exterior finishes:

1. Where "broom finish" is indicated on the Drawings, and where no other exterior slab finish is indicated on the Drawings, finish the exposed concrete surface by lightly combing with a medium stiff broom after troweling is complete.

2. Rubbed surfaces shall be provided on all exposed walls and piers. Immediately after forms are removed, exposed surfaces shall be wetted and rubbed with carborundum brick or other abrasive until even, smooth, and uniform in appearance.

3.07 Curing:

As soon as possible after finishing interior slabs, install a curing membrane consisting of a moisture retaining burlap treated for fire resistance and kept continuously moist, or white plastic sheets meeting ASTM C171.

A. Lap all joints six inches, and securely join together.

B. Weight the covering down to prevent damage from the wind.

C. Achieve a completely sealed membrane over the entire slab.

D. Unless otherwise directed by the Designer, keep the curing membrane in place and intact, for at least ten days after placement of concrete, making all inspections and repairs necessary to ensure proper curing.

3.08 Hot Weather Requirements:

A. Placement:

1. Place concrete in accordance with provisions of ACI 305.

2. Do not use concrete with a placing temperature that will cause difficulty from loss of slump, flash set, or cold joints.

3. Maintain a concrete temperature during placement of less than 90 degrees F.

4. Use all means necessary to avoid drying the concrete prior to finishing operations.

3.09 Cold Weather Requirements:

A. Placement:

1. Place concrete in accordance with the provisions of ACI 306.

2. All footings, walls, grade beams, piers, and slabs-on-grade shall be protected from the penetration of frost by use of heaters, insulation, backfill, enclosures, or other means. This protection shall exist throughout the entire construction period. The Designer shall inspect, at his discretion, the frost penetration during construction. If frost shall be shown to be within 6″ of the bottom of any construction in place, the Contractor shall take immediate steps to insulate, heat, or otherwise prevent further frost penetration.

3. If the protection provided by the Contractor is inadequate, and frost penetration extends beneath the bottom of the construction, this shall be a basis for rejecting that portion of the work. This rejected work shall be removed and properly replaced at the expense of the Contractor.

3.10 Defective Work:

A. Inspection:

1. Immediately after forms and curing membranes have been removed, inspect all concrete surfaces, and patch all pour joints, voids, rock pockets, form tie holes, and other imperfection before the concrete is thoroughly dry.

2. Do not patch until concrete has been inspected by the Designer.

12
Construction Considerations

This book includes this chapter on construction consider-ations (erection), for purposes of completeness. Logically, each individual manufacturer has different procedures which are suggested for proper erection of "that" system. In some cases, these are proprietary, and certainly the procedures recommended by one manufacturer cannot be directly applied to erecting a competitive system.

However, there are certain aspects of erection of a metal building system that are common to all systems. It is these *general* principles that are treated here.

There are two basic introductory thoughts that must be emphasized in conjunction with the construction process. The first relates to overall project safety. The *mandatory* use of all reasonable safety precautions is essential. This includes, but is not limited to, the following:

- Regular safety meetings with work crews

- Use of basic safety equipment, including:
    Hard hat
    Safety shoes
    Safety belts or safety nets for "high work"
    Safety glasses
    Work gloves
- Observation of OSHA rules and regulations
- Providing first aid equipment at the job site

Over and above the basic value of human life, and concern with injury, it is also good business to avoid any injury. Lost time of experienced personnel is a real detriment to job progress. Industry and company insurance rates can climb with too many lost-time injuries. This reduces both profits and employee incentive. There has been more than one construction firm that has been forced out of business *solely* as a result of poor safety practices.

The second introductory concept relates to having adequate tools and equipment available for the erection process. Certainly not every project and every contractor will need exactly the same equipment, but the following are deemed basic. The contractor should recognize that both wood and metal work will be involved in every project, with the wood used for temporary bracing, forming, dunnage, etc.

The following is considered a minimum list of basic tools required for the erection of the typical metal building system:

- A complete set of socket wrenches for the many bolting operations involved.
- A spud wrench for bolting, and to aid in alignment.
- Adequate electrical cords, outlets and a portable generator if necessary.
- A cutting torch—for emergency fit up, of course.
- Metal cutter (tin snips).
- A variety of hack and other metal cutting saws.
- A long carpenter's level.
- A professional quality electric drill.
- An adequate supply of rope, cable, hooks and slings.

In addition to the fundamental tools and equipment listed previously, the builder will be required to have (or rent) a crane and/or a forklift for erection of roof members. The preceding list of basic equipment requirements may, at first glance, appear redundant or simplistic to the casual reader. To the contrary, the brief list illustrates the relatively small number of tools required to *completely* erect the metal building system.

Foundation and Concrete Construction

Some aspects of foundation construction, peculiar to the foundation itself, have been treated in Chapter 8. General principles involved in that chapter related primarily to footing construction and concreting.

This chapter deals more with preliminary construction considerations, especially those associated with layout. It is recognized at the outset that not all metal building system contractors are involved in foundation and concrete construction. This work, in fact, may be "subbed-out" to other construction specialists or a general contractor.

For those builders involved in the construction of foundations and concrete work, the following general guidelines are offered:

1) The foundation system must be level, "square," and properly located. Basic horizontal and vertical control (preferably by a registered surveyor), is critical. A typical interior column footing is designed to have the column exactly at the footing center. If the footing is loaded "off center", uneven soil pressure and additional footing bending can occur. Both are undesirable.

2) Soil borings indicate soil conditions only at the bore hold locations. It is reasonable to encounter soils at varying locations which differ from those determined from the borings. Isolated pockets of poor soils will require foundations to be lowered or moved, or the poor soils will have to be removed, and replaced with properly compacted fill or lean-mix concete.

3) In most cases it is not necessary to form footings. If the soil can be excavated to "reasonably" reflect the required footing

dimensions, forms are not required. (Some building officials *insist* on formed footings, however).

4) The anchor bolts must be properly located. Chapter 8 discusses the use of anchor bolts. The location (horizontally and vertically) is critical, and bolts should be placed by template. Proper footing location followed by "mislocation" of anchor bolts is serious.

5) The rigid frame system generates large horizontal forces. Chapter 8 describes several methods of resisting these forces. The use of "hairpin" bars, anchored to the slab-on-grade is common. The hairpin should be properly located *tightly* around anchor bolts and dowel bars to properly transmit horizontal forces to the slab. Also, congestion in the area of column anchor bolts, where bolts, pier dowels, hairpins and pier ties re-bars are located, must be considered. The authors are aware of a serious failure of a pier, wherein the entire space inside the anchor bolt perimeter was void of concrete, due to the congestion described.

6) The foundation system ultimately gets buried and, unless there are problems, the owner does not see this aspect of his building. ·One of the prominent exposed features of buildings is the slab-on-grade of basementless construction. To many owners, the slab is the most important measure of whether he received a good job. The slab is visible to employees, clients and guests. A poor finish or excessive cracking (even though they do not affect the buildings use or operation), will often be a major complaint, and turn an otherwise first class job into a serious problem.

While this book is not intended to include all aspects of construction, a few comments about achieving a good slab are in order. The following are deemed minimum standards for good concrete floor slab construction:

a) High quality concrete (minimum 5½ sacks per cubic yard cement content).

b) Numerous construction joints to achieve crack control.

c) Slab should not be placed directly on footings, but rather on a cushion of sand, perhaps four inches thick.

d) Proper finishing after the "bleed water" has evaporated (i.e., do not finish too early).

e) Proper curing with plastic sheets for seven days.

f) Use of an appropriate sealer or hardener depending on floor use.

Delivery Considerations

Most builders receive the delivery of the metal building system by shipment in a prescribed, and carefully thought out, packing arrangement. Items are usually grouped, and may be packed in the reverse order required for the job, so that items may be removed from the vehicle, and installed. In some instances, they may be packed for ease of site storage prior to erection.

The builder should, upon receipt of the building components, immediately inspect for damage. There are several important reasons for this step in the process. First, claims with the carrier should be filed promptly, so that losses can be covered. Second, and more important, a damaged item may be critical in the erection process. It must be back-ordered, so as not to hold up the job. (Clearly, inspecting for missing items is as important as looking for damage, for the same reason).

It is essential to recognize that each delivered item was intended to be handled in a particular way. This means care must be given as to how an item is picked up, (at what "pick-up points"), as well as how it is stored on the site. Many slender unsymmetrical items, even of steel, can twist and permanently deform if not properly handled. Some members must be stored in a flat, rather than sloped, condition. Availability of proper slings for handling is essential. Something placed on the ground will eventually have to be lifted up for erection. Settlement of inadequate wood dunnage into the soil, (or mud), will create serious handling problems.

Site storage layout is another important factor. Routinely, items are taken from a delivery and stored. Ideally, they should be placed near to where they are needed, so they will not be required to be moved a second time. Moreover, they should not be "in the way" of reasonable erection procedures, so as to slow down the erection process. Thus, a good *pre-planned* site layout is essential for delivery, site storage, assembly and erection. In this context, the reader should recognize that there are often different types of the same class of member. Thus, careful scrutiny is essential, as it would be easy to create serious erection problems by "burying" key building elements.

Pre-Erection Planning

Prior to moving one piece from site storage, it pays to carefully "build the building in your head."* The plans should be carefully studied in terms of determining the type of primary framing system used, which members are critical to brace primary members during erection, what types of secondary framing members are used (i.e., C's or Z's for girts and purlins), what is the bracing system for the completed structure, what type of "skin" is used, (i.e, pre-assembled panels, part masonry, standing seam roof, etc.), and what accessories are included. Each aspect requires special attention and concern.

At this stage, it is also important to check that anchor bolts, footings, grade beams, masonry or concrete walls, etc. are "right on." The time to correct a problem of this nature is before the "iron" goes up. The same kinds of concerns relate to overall geometry, set backs, spacings, etc.

Structural Steel Erection

Subsequent to insuring that the foundations, walls, and anchor bolts are correct, the erection process can begin. As stated previously, only *generalized* procedures can be described, but the first step usually involves the setting of columns. This is commonly done with either a crane, a fork lift, dollies, or in some cases, by hand.

Next, wall girts are placed to stabilize and plumb the columns. In this context, it is important to mention that much of the wall/girt assembly can be pre-assembled on the ground. A worker can "produce" several times the erected output on the ground, rather than on a ladder.

---

* The metal building system industry has independent erection specialists available who have extensive experience in this area. It may pay to consult one of these specialists at the planning stage.

After acheiveing a stable wall system, the endwall rafters are erected. The endwall is, of course, stabilized by the perpendicular wall construction. Thus, the endwall rafter is "automatically" stable. Interior rafters are next erected in conjunction with roof purlins, and the eave struts are generally the last framing members to be erected.

Often the "stability" of the metal building system is achieved by cross-bracing. Such bracing can be installed with the columns, with the structure automatically being braced during the erection process. The "plumbness" of columns should be constantly checked during erection. A carpenter's level is indispensable during this phase.

Erection of Sheeting

Although the various types of wall and roof sheeting systems have been described elsewhere in this manual, the authors do wish to emphasize that, like the slab-on-grade, the sheeting is visible. Often, much of the structure is covered, and the owner sees only the exposed sheeting. The advantage of doing a good job with the finish is obvious.

Also, the sheeting (used here in the broad sense to include walls and roofs) is the source of one of the few problems owners commonly experience with buildings; namely, leaks. To minimize this occurence, and the associated call-back, a number of positive steps can be followed:

- Bolted connections must be *properly* tightened for structural, as well as operational, reasons. This involves use of both the right tools *and* the proper torque.

- Sealants must be properly used at locations of fasteners and seams.

- Fasteners should be properly and uniformly aligned. A good alignment of fasteners is essential to good appearance.

- In general, the girts and purlins are not suitable for climbing, or support of ladders. The C's and Z's are especially susceptible to damage (rotation and lateral buckling) due to their shape.

- In general, it is a good policy to erect the sheeting in a direction moving away from the principal view. Also, for improved weather tightness, side laps on panels should take into account the direction of the prevailing winds to minimize the chance of water penetration.

- Ideally, most roof systems should not be walked on by workmen. No matter how convenient, the potential for damage, (and leaking), is markedly increased by walking on any roof or roofing system.

13

Insurance

A major expense in any business operation today is the payment of premiums for various insurance policies. We insure our lives, our ability to work, our cars, and our homes on a personal basis. The availability of the various types of insurance, and the complex procedure by which rates are established, is reason enough to include the topic of insurance here. Moreover, as pointed out in the discussion on life cycle costing, insurance is a recurring cost. Constructing a low first-cost combustible structure, with high yearly insurance premiums, may easily result in a high life cycle cost.

Insurance — A Definition

Insurance is defined as a contract between two parties whereby one party, (the insurer), indemnifies (gives security against or frees from the consequences of) the other party, (the insured), against the occurrence of a particular stipulated act. The insurer will pay money to the insured if the specified event occurs—thus creating some loss to the insured. The insurer literally *gambles* that not all of the people insured will suffer losses at the same time. By analyzing statistics, such as death, injury, fire, or accident, an insurer can establish the expected frequency of the occurrence of the event, and determine what charges must be made to the insured parties, so that sufficient funds will be available in the event that a particular event occurs. Such studies of statistics are called *actuarial studies,* and it is from these studies that insurance rates are established.

Insurance Carriers

Prior to discussing detailed provisions of the various types of insurance available, for purposes of completeness, this section on insurance carriers is included. It is intended that the reader can become familiar with the types of carriers, and the philosophical differences in each organization.

The principal types of carriers for any type of insurance can be grouped into four main categories:

- Mutual Companies
- Stock Companies
- Co-operatives
- Individual Underwriters

Mutual Companies

This carrier is a corporation which is owned by the policyholders. No stock or stockholders exist. Policyholders' premiums are used to pay losses. Exess in premiums over losses is returned to the policyholders in the form of "dividends." These are *not* like stock dividends, and no income tax is paid on the dividend value, since they really reflect a return of overcharging for the premium.

Today, most mutual companies write *non-assessable policies.* In prior years, mutuals wrote *assessable policies,* which meant that if additional funds were required to pay policy losses, the policyholders could be assessed. This is less prevalent today, although some assessable policies, (for one additional premium), can still be found in existence.

Stock Companies

These are corporations which operate as any profit making business. Stockholders invest capital which, added to premiums, is used to pay losses. Premiums are firmly fixed, and no "dividends" exist.

Co-operatives

This is an offshoot of the mutual company concept. The insureds deposit premiums into a reserve to pay losses. Each member has his own account from which losses are paid. If losses exceed reserves, members must contribute proportionately (to the amount of annual premium), sufficient funds to bring the reserves to an adequate level.

Individual Underwriters

This concept is the method used by Lloyd's of London. Lloyd's issues no policies, but *arranges* for individual underwriters to undertake a portion of the risk for the various insureds. The underwriter's own wealth is the backing for the insurance.

There is one other method by which insurance can be provided. This is known as *self insurance,* whereby the individual puts his own money into a fund (bank account), out of which losses are to be paid. This is a form of insurance only if the fund actually exists and is maintained.

Metal Building System Insurance Considerations

There are several types of insurance which relate to the metal building system as an insured risk. Insurance can be purchased which protects against losses from fire, wind damage, floods, vandalism, collision, and earthquake, just to mention a few. If insurance can be purchased to insure Jimmy Durante's nose, only imagination is the limit as to the extent of insured risks. This book will include considerable emphasis on *fire,* due to the dominant effect of this risk on the industry. Also included will be a treatment of Extended Coverage Insurance and Earthquake Insurance.

Fire Insurance and Fire Rating Bureaus

Most insurance carriers establish their charges (premiums) by using rates set by rating bureaus. Some individual underwriters and firms in self insurance programs set their own rates.

There are several rating bureaus which generate rates, and

several different methods by which rates can be generated. Rating bureaus, as of this writing, include:

- Insurance Services Office (ISO)
- Several Independent State Rating Bureaus
- Industrial Risk Insurers (IRI)
- Factory Mutual (FM)

Each develops ratings in a different way, and for different types of risk.

One method of generating rates is to analyze the statistical data compiled as a result of many fires, and to publish the rates in a rating manual. This procedure is commonly used for smaller projects. While simple to apply, the method does deal with *averages*. A good building will lose, and a poor building will gain, (in terms of premium costs), under such a system.

A superior method is to rate each project on an individual basis, which is known as *specific rating*. The specific rate is dependent on such factors as the type of building system, contents, protection, and exposure. These concepts will be elaborated upon in subsequent sections. ISO has established a rating system known as the "Commercial Fire Rating Schedule" (CFRS), which has been adopted by most states as the basis for their individual rating schedules. Each state then applies their own factors to arrive at the final insurance rates for facilities under their jurisdiction.

IRI and FM not only rate projects, but insure them as well. In order to be insured, a building must meet requirements set down by these organizations. IRI has a staff of rating engineers which inspects all properties, and produces reports outlining the required recommendations for upgrading the property to receive the lower insurance rates. FM has developed rules with which a building must comply in order to receive FM insurance. FM maintains an extensive test facility which it uses to establish and verify its various building and contents requirements.

Fire Ratings

Prior to discussing fire rates, it may be helpful to acquaint the reader with fire ratings of building components. In this country, the fire ratings or classification of various materials of construction are established by the American Society of Testing and Materials (ASTM) to the extent that state, local, and model building codes insist on having construction meet specific ASTM requirements. ASTM has prescribed the requirements for a *standard fire* in its Publication of Committee E-119. This standard fire is described in a "time-temperature" curve as illustrated in Figure 13-1.

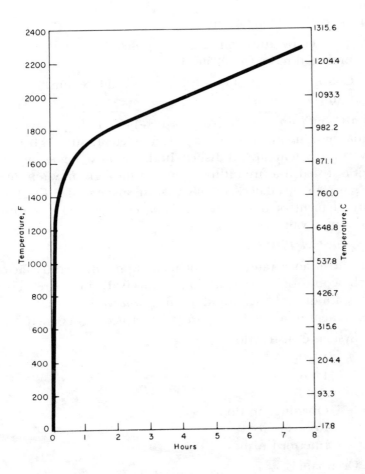

Figure 13-1. ASTM E-119 Time-Temperature Curve

When subjected to this "standard fire," building components must perform in a specified way to achieve a fire rating. For example, if a floor system is to achieve a two-hour rating, it would be subjected to a fire test. Such tests are made at approved testing laboratories, such as at Underwriters Laboratories (UL), Ohio State University, and others.

As an example in a fire test, the floor assembly is subjected to temperatures per the E-119 fire curve. If a two-hour rating is to be achieved, the following conditions must exist during the two hours:

1) No collapse may occur.

2) The temperature on the unexposed face may not have increased more than 250° F.

3) Cotton waste spread on the unexposed face must not have ignited.

If all conditions are satisfied, a two-hour rating is awarded. Similar tests are made on walls, columns, etc. Results of fire tests for various systems are published. In this context, it is essential to point out that if a fire rating is known for a given *system* (e.g., concrete slab, metal deck, open web joist, suspended ceiling), and if *any* element of that system is then changed, the fire rating is no longer valid.

Fire Insurance Rates

Fire insurance rates are dependent upon numerous factors which would affect the building "survival" in a fire. These factors are quite logical, and are not *equally* important to the development of a rate for a particular project. They include:

- System Construction
  - Walls
  - Floors
  - Roofs
  - Openings in floors
  - Roof surface
  - Interior finishes
- Occupancy
- Exposure to other fire hazards

- Protection
    Fire Departments
    Hydrants
    Extinguishers
    Alarms
    Sprinklers

These various factors are applied using a system of points and percentages for determining a rate for the building, including its contents. The rate established is called the "80 percent co-insurance rate." Under this concept, the policyholder agrees to carry insurance to at least 80 percent of the value of the property being insured. If at the time of a loss, less than 80 percent is carried, the *insured* pays for the loss, to the extent that the amount of insurance is less than the 80 percent value. It is possible to insure up to 100 percent for addition premiums.

Construction Systems

The Construction Fire Rating System (CFRS) classifies buildings into six categories:

Construction Class	Type	Description
6	Fire Resistive	2-hour fire resistive walls, floors, and roof
5	Modified Fire Resistive	1-hour fire resistive walls, floors, and roof
4	Masonry Non-Combusitble	1-hour fire resistive walls; non-combustible or slow burning walls, floors, and roof
3	Non-Combustible	Non-combustible or slow burning walls, floors, and roof
2	Jointed Masonry	1-hour fire resistive walls; combustible floors and roof
1	Frame	Combustible walls, floors, and roof; or non-combustible or slow burning walls with combustible floors and roof

Rates increase from class six to class one. An examination of the descriptions shows the importance of walls in establishing a rate. Metal building systems routinely fall into construction class three, but by use of combustible walls, a class one rating could result.

There are ISO offices in most states, and not all are consistent in their method of rating. When combining a basic metal building system with various wall systems, it is essential to contact the local ISO office for help. The important point to recognize here is that a wide range in ratings for both building and contents can be achieved by varying wall and roof construction, and fire protection for columns.

Prior to 1975, published classifications by Underwriters Laboratories did not include fire resistance ratings for column sizes less than W 10 x 49. Also, no test documentation was available for tapered columns of variable weight and cross-sectional areas.

Column Type	Flange	Web	Layers of ½″ Type C Gypsum Wallboard	Rating,* Hours	UL Listing
Built-up	4 x 3/16	5⅝ x .09	3	2	X524
	4 x 3/16	6⅝ x ⅛	3	2	
	4 x 3/16	23⅝ x ⅛	3	2	
	4 x 3/16	23⅝ x ⅛	2	1	
	6 x ½	35 x 3/16	3	2	
	7 x ¼	59½ x ¼	3	2	
	7 x ¼	59½ x ¼	2	1	
Pipe		4″ Diameter t = .109	2	1½	X531
Cold-Formed Channel		7″ x 3″ x .066	3	2	X530
		7″ x 3″ x .066	2	1	

*Applies to either parallel or non-parallel flange columns.

Table 13-2. Summary of Column Fire Test Results

The Metal Building Manufacturers Association has since made several column fire tests at UL on various kinds of metal building system columns, and obtained ratings for one and two hours. A complete list of these tests is shown in Table 13-2. In addition to rating tests, MBMA conducted a fact-finding test in December, 1978, to determine the effect of three-sided column protection, and unprotected girts penetrating the column protection. As a result of this test, Underwriters Laboratories has modified the previous listings to include three-sided protection and girt penetration without disturbing the previously developed ratings.

In addition to the columns actually tested, Underwriters Laboratories has determined by engineering investigation that *all* columns meeting the following specifications will afford the protection indicated:

Built-up Columns

Minimum Web Thickness .... .090 inches

Minimum Web Depth .... 5.625 inches

Minimum Flange Thickness .... .1875 inches

Minimum Flange Width .... 4.0 inches

Maximum Web Depth .... 59.5 inches

Minimum W/D .... .238 inches

Where:

W = cross-sectional area (ft^2) x 490 (16/ft^3)

D = (4 x flange width) + (2 x web depth) – (2 x web thickness)

Pipe Columns

Minimum Diameter .... 4.0 inches

Minimum Wall Thickness .... .109 inches

Cold-Formed Columns

Minimum Size .... 7.0 inches x 3.0 inches

Minimum Thickness .... .066 inches

Flame Spread

Flame spread may be defined as a measure of the rate at which the flame will spread across a particular surface. It is measured in a laboratory test which rates materials on a scale wherein cement asbestos board is rated "0", and red oak is rated "100". Obviously, the higher the rating, the greater the flame spread.

Finishes have been classified by the National Fire Protection Association (NFPA) as:

Class A .... Flame Spread 0-25

Class B .... Flame Spread 26-75

Class C .... Flame Spread 76-200

If a metal frame building utilizes materials with a high flame spread rating, the overall insurance rating can obviously be adversely affected. Also, even if a material has a low flame spread rating (Class A), but is a "high damage" material, (i.e., severe damage occurs in a fire with foam plastic, fabrics, etc.), high insurance rates may result. Clearly, a high damage material with a high flame spread surface will attain the worst possible rates. Thus, a metal building system (Class 3) with combustible walls could be classified as frame construction (Class 1). It should be clear that flame spread of wall and ceiling materials can have a profound effect on fire ratings, and ultimately, on the competitiveness of the metal building system.

Occupancy Considerations

As stated previously, various factors affect fire rates besides the building's construction. A significant factor is the building occupancy. It should be obvious to the reader that a building storing paint or chemicals would have a higher fire rating than one storing flat steel sheets. Similarly, the manufacturing of paint or other chemicals is more hazardous than storing them.

Occupancy affects insurance rates, both by the actual occupancy use which defines the hazard, *and* by the contents. Some contents would be unaffected by a fire, while others may disintegrate in seconds. The key consideration is that different occupancies and contents can dramatically affect fire insurance rates.

Exposure Considerations

By "exposure" is meant the susceptibility that a particular building has to being involved in a fire which starts in an adjacent structure. The factors which affect the rating that a building gets due to its *exposure* include:

1) Distance between buildings—if buildings are far enough apart, no exposure charge results.

2) Combustibility of the exposing structure, including wall openings.

3) Occupancy of the exposing structure.

4) Combustibility of the exposed structure—a building with non-combustible walls, but with many openings, is more likely to be involved in a fire from an adjoining building than a windowless building.

5) Protection of the exposing structure—buildings with automatic sprinklers radiate no exposure.

Thus, fire ratings *can* be affected by exposure. By careful site planning, fire rates can be reduced, (i.e., locate buildings far from those with high exposure problems).

Public Protection Concepts

Clearly, a building's fire insurance rate would be drastically affected by the fire protection available to the area. Such factors as availability of a public water supply, Fire Department, Police Department, local building codes, fire alarm systems, general community considerations, and ease (or difficulty) of access to site, will all affect the quality of public fire protection.

It is important to recognize that for a particular site, the public protection available would affect the insurance rate comparably for any building system, and is not a factor in comparing alternative systems.

Internal Protection Concepts

There are many things that can be provided inside a building to add to the fire safety. Among these are:

Fire alarms

Fire extinguishers

Smoke detectors

Water standpipes

Fire doors and compartmentation

Automatic sprinkler systems

Each method, whereby internal protection is improved, can result in reduced fire ratings.

Of the previously listed protective systems, the automatic sprinkler is the most dominant in terms of its impact on fire ratings. Since ratings and resulting premiums are constantly changing, no specific dollar values will be given. However, certain general comments can be made about the "benefits" of sprinkler systems.

Sprinkler systems are costly. However, most rating bureaus will reduce insurance premiums substantially (60% or greater reductions are possible) if sprinklers are installed. Thus, a sprinkler system can be "paid for" through reduced insurance premiums. Depending on the construction system, it is possible to have the insurance premium savings pay for the sprinklers in as little as one year, or as long as 15 or more years.

There are some secondary benefits which result from the installation of an automatic sprinkler system. These benefits have come to be known as "trade-offs." Many building codes permit reductions in other building requirements in buildings with sprinkler systems. These include:

- Reduction of dividing firewalls
- Reduction in number of exits
- Reduction in distances to exits
- Reduction in flame spread requirements
- Reduction in hourly ratings for certain members

As of this writing, many codes are reviewing the concept of trade-offs, but there is no question that they can have an economic impact which favors the installation of sprinklers.

The authors wish to emphasize that the installation of an automatic sprinkler system should *not* be viewed as a *guarantee* against fire damage, or improvement in the life safety characteristics of the building. Under no conditions should such claims be made to a prospective customer. The *economic* advantages of the sprinkler system are real, however.

Contents Considerations

This book previously noted that *contents* can have a major impact on insurance rates. Contents rates are, in fact, usually greater than building rates.

Contents can not only be damaged by fire, but by smoke and water as well. As a result, two types of classifications are used in rating contents. The first is the *combustibility* class. This relates to the ease with which the contents will burn and contribute to the fire fuel. Five classes of combustibility are used; from Class 1 (non-combustible, such as storing bricks) to Class 5 (flash burning, such as a chemical factory).

Another factor affecting contents rate is the damage susceptibility due to fire, smoke, or water. Some materials might burn with some difficulty, but be damaged instantly by smoke or water. Again, five classes exist, from Class 1 (minimal damage, such as a heavy steel fabricator) to Class 5 (extreme loss, such as in a flower shop).

Contents rates are never less than the building rates. As a metal building systems contractor cannot affect contents rates, this section is included only for completeness.

Extended Coverage Insurance

Extended coverage insurance covers perils such as windstorm, hail, explosion, riot, strikes, civil commotion, collision, and smoke. Of these, the dominant peril which affects rates is wind. Extended coverage may not be obtained separately, but must be an extension of the basic fire policy. The reason that wind is the dominant factor in rate determination is that the other perils are too difficult to assess.

High winds can cause severe damage to buildings, but the dominant concern relates to wind uplift. As the air flows over the roof of a building, uplift forces are created similar to those which lift an aircraft. These forces vary with building and roof shape. Underwriters Laboratories has tested roof systems, and classifies them as to their uplift resistivity as follows:

UL Class	Rating
90	Wind Resistive
60	Semi-Wind Resistive

Most states either recognize the UL ratings, or have similar ratings adjusted for local conditions, and the ISO offices correspondingly rate extended coverage in three levels according to wind resistivity. Metal building systems incorporating a Class 90 roof will receive the lowest possible extended coverage rate.

Earthquake Factors

Certain areas of the United States are subject to possible earthquakes. The ISO publishes "earthquake rates." Clearly, such locations as Southern California, Alaska, and Southern Missouri will be subjected to the highest rates.

In addition to the effect of location, the building construction system is also a dominant factor in establishing earthquake rates. (A building under construction receives a different rate than a completed structure.) In this context, (and without providing a detailed treatise of seismic design considerations), it is *most important* to recognize that metal building systems do extremely well in terms of earthquake ratings. This is clearly a marketing tool which can be utilized.

Insurance for the Metal Building Contractor

This book is not intended to be a textbook on insurance. However, the intent is to provide the reader with general knowledge about the types of insurance which are available, and perhaps required, in the metal building system business.

Basic coverage may include some or all of the following:

Personal Insurance

Life Insurance for Employees and Principals (to benefit families)

Disability Insurance for Employees and Principals (to benefit employees)

Life Insurance for Employees and Principals (key man insurance to provide funds during the period of replacement of a key individual)

Life Insurance for Principals (to handle the payment to beneficiaries with ownership interest in a business)

Group Health Insurance for Employees and Principals (medical and hospitalization insurance)

Business Insurance

All employers are liable under the law for acts of their employees, and for defective products which create losses for purchasers. Such negligent acts can be insured against. This includes an employee's use of a car, as well as accidents which occur to visitors in the insured's facilities. Typically, all of the preceding types of losses can be covered under a broad form, general liability policy.

Builder's Risk Insurance

Builder's risk insurance is that insurance taken out by the owner on behalf of both owner and contractor to protect both parties during the construction process. This insures against common perils (e.g., fire, vandalism, damage, etc.) occurring while construction is underway. Builder's risk insurance protects all parties concerned until the owner's permanent insurance takes over upon project completion.

Profession Liability Insurance

This is a special type of insurance carried by design professionals. It is also referred to as "errors and omissions insurance." The laws of the various states differ widely on interpretation of the laws regarding liability of designers, but one thing is certain;

design professionals are *personally* liable for negligent acts which they commit. They cannot develop immunity from this liability by incorporating or developing some other form of business entity. Only through insurance can the designer be protected.

Professional liability insurance is extremely expensive. The premium for this insurance is dependent upon certain basic factors which include:

- General losses experienced in the particular design field (e.g., architectural, structural, mechanical, etc.)
- Losses experienced in the state of the policyholder
- Size of the design firm (larger means greater premiums)
- Annual billings
- Type of work (foundation design, tunneling, and long span bridges generate higher premiums)

Only a few carriers will underwrite professional liability insurance. These include, among others:

- Continental Casualty (CNA)
- Lloyd's of London
- Design Professionals Insurance Corporation (DPIC)
- Northbrook Insurance Co.
- Sequoia Insurance Co.

Most policies include an upper limit of coverage with a deductible. Unlike liability insurance for contractors, attorney's fees are *part* of the deductible in professional liability insurance.

As in other forms of insurance, it is possible to "self-insure" against professional liability insurance claims. There is, at the time of this writing, considerable incentive to permit before-tax funds to be set aside in a reserve fund to handle liability claims.

Most liability policies are written on a "claims made" basis. This means that whoever insures the designer *at the time a claim is filed* is liable, independent of when the design error was made.